A BRAIN GONE WRONG

HOPE FOR THE TROUBLED TEEN

DR. W. DEAN BELNAP

Send inquiries to:
Meridian Publishing
www.meridianbooks.net
10504 Sideburn Court
Fairfax, VA 22032-2600
USA

Printed in the United States of America
ISBN: 978-1-934537-04-6

Cover Design: Ron Hoopes, One Company Design (1cd.com)
Interior design: Anastasia Tyler

I dedicate this book to
Scot and Maurine Proctor of Meridian Magazine
and to my loving wife, Elen

Table of Contents

List of Illustrations

Acknowledgments

Joy and happiness is being married for eternity—having wonderful children, grandchildren and great grandchildren. I am grateful to my wife, Mary Elen, our children Rosann, Paul, Louise, Eric, Grant, David and their spouses. I'm also grateful for the encouragement and professional guidance of Scot and Maurine Proctor, Heidi Swinton and Becky Harding—they have been invaluable.

And to all of you, our friends—My wish is that this book will help guide the relationships within your families to an eternal destiny.

Preface

Is There Hope?

"I have witnessed the healing power of the Lord."

I NEVER EXPECTED TO FIND MYSELF IN A TESTIMONY MEETING of psychiatrists in the Ivy League Halls of Harvard. And yet, there I was, surrounded by my colleagues from all over the country, sharing experiences and feelings about faith and healing. We had been invited to the university to attend a seminar as part of the creation of the "Mind and Body Medical Institute." This new department, formed by faculty members from the Departments of Psychiatry and Internal Medicine, declared its purpose—to teach patients and physicians how to use "religion, faith, prayer and spirituality to aid in the healing of the mind and body."

Although the mind/body connection, as it applies to faith and healing, had been previously explored in the media, such a contemporary movement was unprecedented among academic and medical circles. After my profession had drifted towards a secular approach during the 20th century, to witness the medical shift back to a more religious and sectarian paradigm infused me with excitement and hope. Harvard, and the 52 other universities adopting similar programs into their curriculum, had given academic legitimacy to concepts of faith, I had embraced since my youth.

For decades in my private medical practice I have treated and counseled teens who are on the edge; many who are over the edge. I have counseled them as they have sought to get their lives back—and on track. For most of my patients and their families, the effort has been the toughest work they have ever done or ever will do. Not only are they reshaping aberrant behavior, they are working with a "brain gone wrong" because of their bad choices.

In addition, there are youth who came into the world with challenges they did not create for themselves. They too face a "brain gone wrong." While society has begun to recognize their issues, it has yet to identify the best ways of helping these precious children realize their potential. They too deal with the invisible—from autism to learning disabilities, from physical challenges to a mind that thinks or processes differently, facing darkness and depression that is gene driven.

All my life I have been blessed to witness the power of the Lord in healing both the mind and the body. That faith was borne of a rich spiritual tradition given by my parents. Greater faith was honed and personalized through medical school and a lifetime of practicing medicine. That same faith crystallized as I pursued humanitarian and church service opportunities.

Rewiring a "brain gone wrong" is both possible and necessary to allow each youth to cope with and contribute to a better world. What is required is a "mighty change" working within. The power of the Atonement can diminish the effects of a string of bad and destructive choices. With faith in the Lord Jesus Christ and his Atonement, hope can replace hopelessness and peace can most certainly come. The ancient prophet Isaiah declared the Lord would "keep him in perfect peace, whose mind is stayed on thee, because he trusteth in [the Lord]" (Isaiah 26:3).

So must it be with our youth. They must turn to the Lord for healing as well as for strength and courage. And it will come as it has through dispensations past. "And they all cried with one voice, saying: Yea, we believe all the words which thou hast spoken unto us; and also, we know of their surety and truth, because of the Spirit of the Lord Omnipotent, which has wrought a mighty change in us, or in our hearts, that we have no more disposition to do evil, but to do good continually" (Mosiah 5:2).

I experienced one of my earliest "imprintings" of faith during the Great Depression. Our family faced the severe anxiety—shared with others—would we survive? As I watched my father pray, I knew we would be all right. My father's faith was my assurance. I have often reflected on stories of faith and healing in our family. One such story involved my uncle, Francis Belnap, who through prayer and the power of the priesthood, called his son back to life several hours after the boy died of rheumatic fever. This occurrence, as well as other sacred family experiences, laid a foundation of faith for me that was augmented during medical school. At this time, I read a composite of spiritual experiences of healing in Man the Unknown by Alexis Carrell, a Nobel Prize-winning surgeon from France. He testified of observing a cancer shrivel to a scar following the prayerful appeals of an afflicted woman. Later, my wife, Elen, and I experienced a similar miraculous event while serving a mission in Indonesia. A sister who had contracted a breast cancer, which had grown to the size of an orange, was given a blessing. A few weeks later, the cancer was gone, leaving a scarred indentation of equal size to the original cancer.

While these experiences seemed natural and right to me, they have for many years seemed foreign and anecdotal to the medical profession. Not anymore. What explanation could there be for such a shift?

One of the determinants revealed at the seminar was the gradual slip away from Freudian Analytical Psychiatry. Indeed, the head of the Department of Psychiatry made direct reference to this drift as he described the move from classical Freudian analysis to a development of the integrated Behavioral Sciences. He declared that Freud espoused the thinking of the German philosophers who had proclaimed, "God is dead!" With some degree of humor and a slight smile he said, "Now Freud is dead!" The implication was clear. We were now entering a new era of faith-based medicine, emphasized, addressed, and acknowledged on a collegiate research level.

New and sophisticated research techniques and tools yeild additional reasons for the impetus to study faith and healing within the context of medicine and the mind/body connection. One of these research tools involves neuroimagery of the brain. This neuroimagery is capable of observing and mapping the brain while the whole nervous system is carrying out its functions. These are not just fixed pictures of brain anatomy, but living, moving images. With the help of this tool, neuro-scientists have been able to empirically see that the right side of the frontal brain is activated through prayer and meditation.

This part of the brain, so uniquely human, is the processing point of experiences and value judgments of right and wrong. Neuro-scientists can observe the chemistry of brain and body reciprocally interacting. They understand what happens to the patient, but the how and the why remain a scientific mystery. This evidence with its commensurate scientific dilemma has prompted many neuro-scientists to conclude that the brain and the "soul" work together as the mind of man and that spiritual forces must and do exist. That such concepts are even acknowledged is spectacular! One last notable finding to come out of the university research indicates that when the physician, practitioner, and patient share a common personal belief and faith, the results are even more striking.

I have personally witnessed the validity of such evidence as I have become involved during the past three years in humanitarian service. This service, in part, has included work with LDS missionaries struggling with mental health issues. Other service has included work with non-profit agencies which also help with mental health problems. These organizations are directed to members of the Church. In a setting where personnel, physicians, and patients all share the same belief system, the rewards and results are enormous. For us, the "why" and the "how" are no mystery. Addictions to pornography, gambling or substance abuse can be surmounted. Mental illnesses such as depression and bipolarity can be managed and even eliminated. The work is hard. It is humbling. But at the same time, it has brought me more joy than any other medical service with which I have been engaged. Both patients and caregivers have all found that there is a continued need for another essential member of the team—the Holy Spirit; for ultimately, it is the Lord who heals.

Malachi poetically prophesied that all would be made right when the Lord returns again, "with healing in his wings." Yet, even now, in this life, our physical and mental travails can find healing in this same faith and hope. As we serve each other in this capacity, we are his servants.

This book explores the issues of mental health and mental illness among our teens. There are three sections. Section One addresses "a brain gone wrong" by personal choices of behavior including addictions. Section Two discusses the challenges of "a brain gone wrong" by its own development, or as a result of adversities imposed on children in their early years through no fault of their own. Both are critical to understanding the challenges facing youth today. These chapters may also be helpful in flagging potential destructive behaviors or identifying existing syndromes. Section Three offers help—and hope—for these perilous times. While medical intervention can be very helpful, it is only half the solution. We must turn our hearts and homes back to the one true source of healing power. The more secure we become in our faith in God, the greater is our willingness to let his ways become our ways. Faith in God then becomes the ultimate power source for healing the "brain gone wrong."

—Dr. W. Dean Belnap

Why Today's Teen Is in Trouble

"Know ye not that ye are the Temple of God, and that the spirit of God dwelleth in you?"

—*1 Corinthians 3:16*

THE 21ST CENTURY FACES A WAR with no name and no marked battleground. The casualties are legion; they are our youth. They come from every address and ability and are being squandered in what was once considered the lifestyle of only a sullied few. Our feel-good culture, eroded by bad behavior, bad choices—and for many teens a succession of very bad days—has drugs, alcohol, suicide, eating disorders, violence and the occult just a quick step from the corner lemonade stand. Teens are raised amid decay in families, schools, and the streets on which they live or roam. Gangs have stepped in to fill the void of families; media, fashion, peer pressure and popularity now dictate what were once decisions made at the kitchen table. The scenes are ugly, scarred and riddled with pain. Youth are forced to live beyond their years and to make decisions not even contemplated by their parents: Do I drink? Take meth? Smoke? Join a gang? Bring a gun to school, or even stay in school? Do I distinguish myself by my dress, tattoos, the color of my hair, or my sexual preferences? Do I keep the baby, give it up for adoption or abort? Should I consider suicide because my life is sad and hopeless? Many youth survive the onslaught; too many do not.

In many cases, a youth's tender—and still learning—brain is caught up in a downward spiral and is actually rewired. Without help, the teen is caught in the trap of the "brain gone wrong."

Who failed the youth with birthright and promise? Parents? The system? The entertainment industry? Friends? Religious leaders? School administrators and teachers? Indeed, society struggles with blurred lines of right and wrong and in many cases, no wrong at all. Our youth reflect our self-indulged culture.

The radical shifts of the last century have shaped a culture that cares less, craves more, and seeks pleasure over peace. Social structures that have grounded our sense of connection are disappearing; communities are collapsing under the weight of youth misusing agency.

Parents who are solid, God-fearing citizens are watching their precious youth slide into the dark abyss that was once considered the underbelly of society. It's not so different for those parents who themselves play close to the edge. Without question, every family is vulnerable.

Counseling loads in the best of communities, as well as the government clinics, are bulging with what we call "troubled" youth. "Troubled" is not even close to the diagnosis. The common terms "at risk" or "acting out" do not even begin to indicate the depth of the problems swirling around teens and families.

Society begs for answers, somewhere to point, someone to blame, and then demands a quick fix for the once ebullient child whose stare is now vacant. Fix. The word is gripping. Fix, a common term for addictive behavior, is in reality, no fix at all. Can you fix a youth whose teenage years have been wasted? Can you reverse the "imprinting" that self-abuse in its many forms has done to imprint their highly sensitive brains? Teens are still a work in progress; both the body and the mind are maturing. Raging hormones are blamed for volatile and surly responses, for existential angst and resentment of authority.

The explanation of what goes on in a teen's head is far more fundamental. The brain a teen begins with is not the one he leaves with at the waning of those tumultuous years. In adolescence, teens develop the ability to plan, to organize, to manage emotions and complex tasks, to understand and even empathize with others, to exercise wisdom and good judgment. This happens not all at once or with just passage of time. It is the essence of learning, the programming of the brain, that gives deference to the singularly human ability to think and act responsibly.

In the past decade science has determined that the brain is not fully locked into patterns established or developed in early childhood. The brain continues to develop during teen years; brain cells and new neural connections take on new life. Between puberty and young adulthood, the prefrontal lobe—what we call the executive portion of the brain responsible for self-control, judgment, emotional regulation, organization and planning—warps into renewed articulation. Teenage years are essentially a second chance to consolidate circuits for mature adult response. Extraneous neural branches get pruned back as a newer and more efficient circuitry takes over.

Teens have power over the pruning process by what they see, what they take in, what they do. It can be positive. Or negative. Teens process information differently from adults. At this phase of development, the ability to catch the football, juggle functions and equations, convert musical scores into finger play, compose poetry and make linguini become both unconscious and enjoyable. Born in these years are the sports enthusiasts, photographers, computer wizards, biologists and architects. Their choices direct and give emphasis to budding interests and, hence, wire their brains for further use.

I call it **imprinting.**

Stamped into their minds—imprinted—is what happened today; what they saw; what they said; what they took in and what they felt. That imprinting is more than memory, more than a series of good and bad days catalogued according to date, time and place. Imprinting is a biological process that takes place in the brain where teens do their most selective thinking. All are born with certain genetic connectors that predispose them to act and think and make decisions and connect those experiences to pleasure or pain. Imprinting acts upon that genetic structure.

Amos in the Old Testament spoke prophetically when he described "a famine and a thirst in the land." So it is today. Youth hunger for things spiritual. They substitute what they cannot find with destructive behaviors, influences and substances that help them feel—feel anything in a darkening and disturbed world. They turn to the tools that the world has created to fill time and space, but those means and measures can never fill the soul. Only God can and will work such miracles.

Chapter 1

Can Imprinting Be Reversed?

"Come unto me all ye . . . heavy laden, and
I will give you rest."

—Matthew 11:28

IMPRINTING CAN BE POSITIVE AND NEGATIVE. While teen years are a time for testing and reaching out to define personal space, that experimenting need not compromise the brain and its extraordinary God-given powers.

Positive imprinting, what brain science calls "forward genetics," changes the brain to ever-developing levels of fulfillment, direction, and goal formation for a continually better future. Positive imprinting—of the prefrontal cortex—correlates to higher intelligence evidenced by the most advanced aspects of human intelligence. These include verbal expression, memory of higher or advanced concepts, abstraction and the ability to formulate behavioral plans and pursue them. For example, charity is a measure of the strength of the prefrontal cortex. Uncharitable acts reflect negative imprinting, a diminished prefrontal lobe.

With the aid of new technology, sophisticated brain imaging techniques can illustrate in real-time pictures the very activation of negative imprinting from one cold beer to a joint, a violent scene played out on the big screen, a pornographic illustration on the family computer. Initially, the stimulation tickles the brain. But for some, far too many, just that one adventure is enough to lock in an imprint that begins the downward spiral. For others, long-term use cuts new pathways to the areas of the brain that control pleasure and judgment. The new routes circumvent the prefrontal lobe and response accelerates to the pleasure center. An addicted brain is both physically and chemically different from a normal brain not subjected to negative imprints. The brain has been reprogrammed to compulsively want more rather than to weigh the options.

Negative imprints erode the ability to feel pleasure in those things that once produced satisfaction. Adolescents whose choices are producing negative imprints hang with others who are in similar frame of mind; they share a code of secrecy. Other signals include being boldly argumentative or sullen; testy or sad; depression; showing less and less interest and motivation in school, even if grades are high; changing eating habits or not eating at all.

Gene combinations make us distinct. Singular gene patterns may, in many instances, be vulnerable to negative imprinting; hence, regressive behavior. Studies have shown that changes take place in the gene make-up of the brain to create temporary or permanent loss of the prefrontal lobe of the brain. In other words, normal behavior such as loss of inhibitions, or urges to satisfy need, feed a habit, or engage in violent behavior, become reality. Imprinting switches the actual DNA, turning it on and off, and in the process, changes the very essence of a teen's identity.

Genes reverse when imprinted with negative experiences or behaviors. Lost are the nerve transmissions that access the unique higher centers where freedom of choice and feelings of joy are centered. Instead, once prosperous brain functions are overridden by primitive, animal-like behaviors. The result is a teen who drinks excessively, takes drugs, finds excitement in violence, seeks company with gangs, uses sex, abuses family and friends and ultimately loses the potential to rise above self-gratification.

Here's what happens: The neurotransmitter dopamine springs from neuron to neuron in the brain circuitry, beaming a molecular "grin" for a feel-good sensation. Its activity affects the firing of other neurons and stimulates feeling from mild pleasure to a surge of energy and euphoria. Drugs—whether cocaine, marijuana, crack, heroin or whatever is the latest craze on the streets—drive straight to the basal ganglia where feeling is stored. Euphoria! For a moment. The process is the same for sexual addictions, alcohol, and violence. The initial experience produces feel-good sensations. But what follows are irritability, anxiety, distress, even despair until the next experience and the next. It is compelling to know that each drug use produces a high, but never one equal to the first. Hence, more drugs, stronger drugs, more frequent ingestion to stimulate, become the pattern but never the panacea.

Such stimulation is the fork in the road. The model is the same for alcohol and other stimulants that open the floodgates for feel-good chemicals like serotonin. The result is resculpting of the brain. Want becomes need. There can never be enough to feed the growing appetite as the pleasure center of the brain pushes the executive center aside. From the prefrontal cortex, the executive decision center, to the basal ganglia, the pleasure center, is a short skip. The brain becomes accustomed to an artificial balance between the two, and programming causes craving as the pleasure center takes over. And it never rests.

Youth who lose the prefrontal cortex control in their brains become addicted to their limbic system, in other words, to stimulation that seeks gratification and coarse pleasure. The change is manifest in every aspect of their lives; relationships, values and purpose are up for grabs as the brain downshifts to this lower level of dependency and need.

The result is sobering. The soul of the nation, as well as individuals, has begun to teeter. A nation watched as students went to school hefting guns and ammo rather than books in backpacks and picked off victims in video game style. With each kill, they cackled and shouted and in the end shot themselves as well. A major source of entertainment for millions is making large numbers of people die on screen. While games used to invite slaughter of gangsters or aliens, today some "games" capitalize on blowing away ordinary people who have done nothing wrong—pedestrians, marching bands, elderly folk. And the saga continues. At some point, the nature of the killing field is no longer animated nor a dress rehearsal. Young people are being invited to enjoy the killing of others. How can a sniper randomly pick off unsuspecting citizens at a gas pump? Because the lines have blurred between real and not real. It has happened across the country. It will happen again because of negative imprints on the brain.

Even after behavior has been reshaped to acceptable patterns, DNA changes may persist. If not too far advanced, brain damage and loss of brain cells can be stopped and genetically rehabilitated. Prolonged negative stimulation may produce permanent results that can even be transferred to those yet unborn. This phenomenon is true of all addictive disorders.

Can a teenager return to that holy image if he or she has compromised the God-given potential?

Yes.

With spiritual help and recognition of moral absolutes, imprinting can be reversed, but it takes adherence to the laws of God and the healing power of his love. That perfect love of the Savior can reshape the soul and its thinking. Just as he helped the blind to see, the lame to walk and the leper to be cleansed, he can remake a "brain gone wrong." He can bring about "mighty change" that will reverse negative imprinting and encourage love, acceptance, humility and tranquility. While therapy, medical treatment, and care centers can help affect long-term change, only the healing power of Jesus Christ can secure the needed revolution. It can come. Jesus Christ's help can bring back much needed balance and security, intimacy of close associations and healthy friendship, physical, emotional and spiritual transformation.

Can it work for a teen who has lost his way and his will to change?

Yes.

The Atonement of Jesus Christ provided for all. The woman at the well and the thieves who hung next to him at Golgotha were restored by his power. Renewal is not limited to those who have only "slightly" erred.

Chapter 2

What Is the Brain?

"It is given unto you to judge that ye may know
good from evil."

—*Moroni 7:15*

IN THE PAST TWO DECADES SCIENCE HAS LEARNED more about the
human brain than was known throughout all prior history. It is clear
that the brain is an incredibly complex physiological mechanism. The
internal structure, which includes the prefrontal cortex, the limbic
system and the basal ganglia, is uniquely human. As previously discussed, the prefrontal cortex is what we call the executive portion of
the brain, and is responsible for self-control, judgment, emotional
regulation, organization and planning; while the limbic system and
basal ganglia are centers that initiate emotions. The limbic system
can either enhance the functions of the prefrontal cortex or act independently with the more primitive basal ganglia that promote and
sustain bad habits. (See Figure 1.)

It happens like this: The neurotransmitter dopamine springs from
neuron to neuron in the brain's circuitry, causing a "feel-good" sensation. That activity prompts the firing of other neurons and stimulates
feeling from mild pleasure to a surge of energy and euphoria.

Who wouldn't want that? The answer is simple—those who want to
be in control of themselves.

The defining characteristic of the human brain and its prefrontal
cortex is the remarkable endowment of free agency and free will.
This feature distinguishes man among all God's creations. The brain

determines how we will act, what we will say, when we will respond and why. God has endowed the human brain with the ability to perceive the difference between right and wrong, good and evil, and positive and negative value systems. These positives and negatives—imprints—are a function of agency.

Addiction, in all its forms, negatively imprints and impairs pure functions of the prefrontal cortex of the brain. Judgment, analysis, agency, comprehension, relationships, conscience and even spirituality are diminished by this encroaching evil.

The brain is the control center of the entire nervous system, the primary sensory apparatus of vision, hearing, touch, taste, and smell. In humans it is an organ of thought. Brains are extremely complex. The human brain contains more than 200 billion nerve cells called neurons, each linked to as many as 185,000 other nerve cells.

In order to understand the complexities of the brain—its actual component parts—consider the descriptions that follow.

What is the prefrontal cortex?

The prefrontal cortex is where moral and value judgments are made. It is located in the anterior part of the frontal lobes of the brain behind the forehead and above the eyes. It is divided into lateral, orbitofrontal, and medial frontal areas. This brain region is the center for planning complex cognitive behaviors, personality expression and moderating correct social behavior. It is unique to humans. Scientific studies link our personalities and responses to the prefrontal cortex.

The basic activity of this brain region is considered to be orchestration of thoughts and actions in accordance with internal goals, morals, values and conscience. That process begins in the right part of the prefrontal cortex. The moral and value judgment made there is then forwarded to the left lobe of the prefrontal cortex.

In the left prefrontal cortex of the brain, we engage in what is called in the brain sciences "inner speech"—in other words, final decision making. The left prefrontal cortex of the brain is the communicator able to send information to any other portion of the brain.

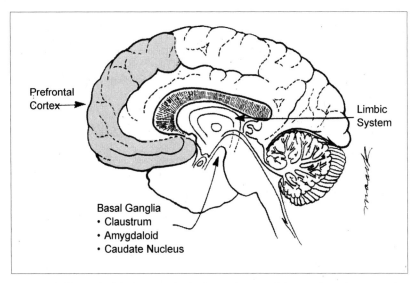

Figure 1. The uniquely human brain is made up of the prefrontal cortex, the limbic system and the basal ganglia. In a mentally healthy state, the prefrontal cortex controls the whole brain and is responsible for self-control, judgment, emotional regulation, organization and planning.

The most typical neurological term for functions carried out by the prefrontal cortex area is executive function. Executive function relates to the ability to differentiate among conflicting thoughts; to determine good and bad, better and best, same and different, and future consequences of current activities; and the ability to work toward a defined goal, to predict outcomes and generate expectations based on socially acceptable behavior.

The chemical that activates the prefrontal nerve functions is serotonin. With addiction, this chemical decreases in the nerve cells while the chemical choline increases in the limbic system and basal ganglia.

What is the limbic system?

The limbic system is the brain area supporting emotional feeling, motivation and association with memory. This system supports the higher areas of the uniquely human prefrontal cortex in experiencing joy. The opposite effect takes place if the individual indulges in addictive behaviors.

The limbic system, activated by the chemical dopamine, operates by influencing the endocrine or glandular system of the body. It also controls the sympathetic nervous system, which flows through all the organs of the body, including the heart, lungs, intestinal tract and sexual organs.

In humans the limbic system can be trained and programmed to serve and enhance the function and higher emotional feelings of the uniquely human prefrontal cortex. On the other end of the scale, it can also be trained and programmed to serve the basal ganglia, and regress to a lower, compulsive, animal-like level defined by the loss of agency and will.

When the structure of nerve cells and DNA change within the limbic and basal ganglia systems, these networks become the source of bodily pleasures, and can lead to addiction. These two areas, when joined together, demand a repetition of indulgence in addictive behaviors in response to temporary and sinful pleasures. In addictions, the limbic and basal ganglia areas take control of the brain. The prefrontal cortex decreases its function, losing its agency and ability to be in charge of actions and behaviors.

In other words, a brain gone wrong.

What are the basal ganglia?

The basal ganglia area is a group of nuclei or focuses of brain cells associated with motor and learning, as well as basic emotional functions. The basal ganglia are also known as the base brain and are largely responsible for our core drives: self-preservation, bodily appetite, fear of death and sensuality. The brain chemical which activates behavior is acetylcholine.

What is the insula?

An additional center which resides in the middle part of the brain along with the limbic and basal ganglia systems is the insula. The insula aids in aligning the limbic system to the basal ganglia and is the center of the "take-over" of those parts of the brain. The medications used to reverse this addictive process and restore function to the prefrontal cortex are selective serotonin re-uptake inhibitors (SSRI). The SSRIs increase the production of serotonin and cause it to remain in the connections of the frontal cortex nerves.

What are neural synapses?

A synapse is a junction used for communication between nerve cells or neurons. Neurons are a major class of cells in the nervous systems, whose main role is to process and transmit information. Neurons are typically composed of a cell body, a dendrite tree, and an axon. (See Figure 2.) Different types of neurons have different shapes and possess specific electrical properties adapted for their specific function and use as neural transmitters.

In the brain, connections—synapses—allow the neurons of the central nervous system to form interconnected neural circuits. These webs are crucial to the biological computations that underlie perception and thought. New thoughts and ideas come from new connections formed in the brain for good or ill behaviors.

Synapses allow nerve cells to communicate with one another through axons and dendrites, converting electrical impulses into chemical signals. The human brain contains a huge number of chemical synapses. Children under ten typically develop close to 1,000 trillion synapses, with that figure declining and stabilizing at about half that amount in adulthood.

How does the brain get rewired?

Upon exposure to a potentially addictive experience, the nerve cells of the basal ganglia secrete an enzyme called corticotrophin-releasing factor, or CRF. The pituitary gland under the basal ganglia is the master gland of all other hormone-producing glands in the body. Stimulated by CRF, the pituitary releases a hormone which races through

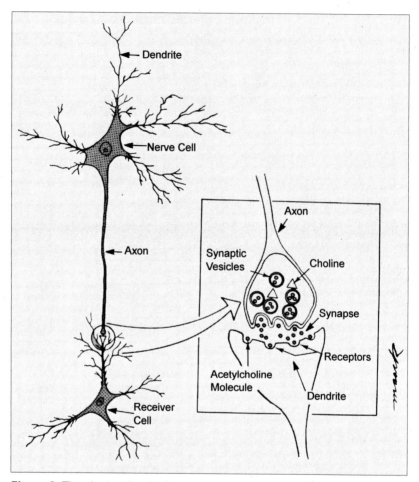

Figure 2. The electro-chemical process between nerve cells in the brain is responsible for thought patterns and behaviors.

the blood stream to the adrenal gland sitting on top of the kidneys. The adrenal gland then excretes steroids which have a marked affect on metabolism and weight gain or weight loss, immune function, heart rate and the behavioral response to stress.

Ideally, the stimulation tickles the brain. But for some, far too many, just that one adventure is enough to lock in an imprint that begins the downward spiral. For others, long-term use cuts new pathways to the areas of the brain that control pleasure and judgment. The new routes bypass the prefrontal lobe and response accelerates by directing the activity directly to the pleasure center. An addicted brain is both physically and chemically different from a normal brain that does not have negative imprints. The brain has been reprogrammed to compulsively want more and more of the addictive experience to search for euphoria.

The prefrontal executive center is pushed aside and loses control. The cravings of the pleasure center take over and it never rests. There can never be enough to feed the growing appetite of the pleasure center of the brain.

Like a computer whose circuitry has been compromised in an endless loop, the chemical transmitter for the frontal areas of the brain, serotonin, decreases to a state of inactivity. The individual loses his conscience, a God-given gift. The basal ganglia and limbic systems persist in their activity and cannot shut off. The "computer" freezes and the response becomes a sensation of continual unpleasant anxiety—the feeling of being stuck is a literal physiological phenomenon.

This anxiety increases the electrical activity of the brain. The normal brain has a cybernating rhythm that circles the entire brain at the average of nine to ten cycles per second. Under stress, that rhythm often increases up to twenty or twenty-five cycles per second. This activity is fatiguing to the brain, particularly the frontal cortex. The brain compensates by shutting down its activity in the areas higher than the basal ganglia and limbic system. In other words, the "computer" crashes. The result is depression.

As the depression/anxiety cycle persists, an indefinite number of nerve cells are lost. The basal ganglia and limbic system no longer serve the prefrontal cortex, but take over control of the brain. Decision-making and freedom of choice are impaired and eventually lost. This process is particularly true in addictive disorders, as the brain in a state of chronic discomfort and apprehension continually "demands" a repetition of the exciting experience.

Ultimately the DNA in the nucleus of the nerve cells undergoes changes that are the same as manifestations seen in mental disturbances and mental illness. The symptoms of chronic fatigue, apathy, agitation, sleeplessness and such auto-immune disorders as fibromyalgia are common in addicts, eventually leading to physical illness as well.

What is addictive behavior?

Addictive behavior is any activity, substance, object or behavior that has become the major focus of a person's life to the exclusion of other activities or behaviors. Addiction is characterized by the repeated use of substances or behaviors despite the clear evidence of harm to self and others secondary to such use.

Current research indicates that there are similarities between physical addiction to various chemicals such as alcohol and heroin and the psychological dependence on activities such as sexual perversions and pornography.

How is addictive behavior developed?

These behavioral activities produce beta-endorphins in the brain generating what is commonly called a "high." The activation takes place in the limbic system and the basal ganglia. Experts suggest that if a person continues to engage in the activity to achieve this feeling of well-being and euphoria, that person is creating an addictive cycle. In so doing, they become physically addicted to their own brain chemicals, thus leading to continuation of the behavior even though it may have negative health or social consequences.

The hypothalamus, one of the basal ganglia, produces chemicals called peptides. These substances within the brain can exceed the effect of externally applied chemicals, alcohol, heroin and others when addictive activities take place. When addictions stimulate an intense craving, chemicals are produced and released in the brain, reinforcing the individual's association with their addictive behavior.

Do we really have a conscience?

The concept of "conscience," once considered out-of-date and out-of-favor has found new acceptance. Modern medicine's discovery of a relationship of mind, body and spirit has elicited acceptance of the existence of a conscience. In increasing numbers, medical experts are publishing their observations as they embrace an endowment of the brain called conscience. They are coming to appreciate that the human prefrontal cortex has the ability to make moral and value judgments, and that the mind can differentiate right from wrong. They are beginning to publicize and call for parents and society to focus on raising children with a "healthy" conscience. Put simply, they are recognizing what mothers and grandmothers have understood for years. Mental health scientists may have shied away from that recognition because of a past refusal to accept spirituality as a force. They now embrace the "relationship of mind, body and spirituality"—another way of describing conscience.

Each of these three aspects of mind, body and spirituality participate in the process of growth and development until the individual reaches maturity. Details of each stage from infancy to adulthood are important to understand as they relate to the uniquely human characteristics of the brain, free agency and moral development.

The first year of life is the most important. A safe relationship to mother and father are imperative to assure survival as well as brain growth, development, and emotional security. Without the warm love of both parents who meet the needs of the infant, there is an actual chance of failure to survive. Those who do survive and have been deprived of developmental structure within an optimal family can experience impairment of brain development during their period of most rapid growth.

The second year of life allows for development of language and early independent exploration. Security comes from loving parental guidance at this stage.

The third phase, from age two until five, is a period of imitative patterning of masculinity and feminity from both parents. A structured relationship in the home with both a father and a mother, each contributing and giving love to their offspring is ideal. Little boys emulate their fathers, while continuing to receive the loving security of mothers. Little girls pattern their feminity from mothers, while enjoying the exemplary relationship with their fathers.

The fourth phase, from age five to eight is one of experiencing love and charity as the child learns to give to others rather than just indulge in self for gratification or dominating relationships.

The fifth phase can then start at age eight, where conscience comes to the realization of right versus wrong. The experiencing of free agency to its fullest extent begins at this time. At age eight the uniquely human prefrontal cortex of the brain is developed and prepared to exercise agency. The years that follow in preadolescence prepare youth for development in a pattern of masculinity or feminity determined by their biological gender.

Adolescence follows with activation of hormones at age eleven to thirteen for girls and for boys two years later. One of the challenges of adolescence is whether to "stay in the nest or leave it."

Each step along the way of optimal growth and development is best achieved when the family is happy and all ages are actively involved in family association and get-togethers such as Family Home Evening. During this period there is a great deal of gratification and growth that comes from parental involvement in activities at school, church, or other places, including arts or sports activities.

We should be alert and active in watching schools, media, entertainment and community programs that would at any time deprive our families or our children of their agency. Watchfulness can aid in maintaining a healthy conscience.

At this point, moral messages and themes should begin to define our children and their choices. Growth and development experiences should include the balancing of morals and values and the determination of concepts of right and wrong.

As parents watch the growth of their children, they draw upon experiences from their own childhood. This leads to easier and more significant communication in the family, particularly when references are made to similarities. Both learn that the conscience is the best storehouse of moral issues and absolutes. All associations in the family, for good or ill, should be guided by pure love.

Discipline at times is needed. That discipline can reveal the disappointment of the parent with anger held to a minimum. The reproof with sharpness should be followed with love. The presence of the Holy Spirit will carry both the disappointment and the peace of forgiveness as the conscience is activated.

Most parents understand this spiritual process. Fortunately, many professionals in all fields of mental and behavioral health acknowledge a "spiritual force" in activating the brain and mind through conscience housed in the prefrontal cortex of the brain.

Maturity brings development of will power, acceptance of authority, and the opportunity to draw from truths of times past. How wonderfully reassuring it is for those us of who use the scriptures as a daily spiritual guide. The moral dilemmas and case histories of the scriptures not only give answers to needs, but guide the development of spiritual endowment—the conscience.

Chapter 3

The Horror of Being Hooked

". . . the hardness of their hearts, and the deafness of their ears, and the blindness of their minds."

—Jarom 1:3

THE STATISTICS OF ADDICTION HAVE REACHED CRISIS STAGE. More than 30 million Americans alive today will become addicted, their brains wrongly rewired wrongly. This includes substance abuse and dependency as well as harmful effects from addictive behavioral disorders like pornography, sexual perversions, gambling, stealing and eating disorders. More than two-thirds of people ages 18 to 25 have used an illegal substance or started down the path of addictive behaviors. Twenty percent of the U.S. population older than eighteen admits to having addictive behaviors. About two-thirds of this group abuses primarily alcohol and the other third preferred substances such as tobacco. Drug abuse of pain-relieving remedies found in most medicine cabinets at home is surging. Derivatives of codeine are very habit forming and can cripple the brain and body.

The use of alcohol, tobacco and illicit drugs causes one out of every four deaths in this country. While tobacco use has dramatically decreased in the adult population, usage by adolescents has been climbing. Illegal drug use costs the nation more than $250 billion dollars a year. The results in a recent study conducted by the National Institute of Health focused on mental health, drug abuse, and other addictive disorders, were staggering. Some 39 percent of the population reported using one or more illicit substances in their lifetime. Thirteen percent had used illicit substances in the past year, and seven percent had used them in the month before the survey was taken.

But the true cost cannot be counted in dollars or percentages. The tragedy of addiction is the ruin of millions of lives, young ones in particular. Unfortunately, it's an easy path to addiction and a tough road to recovery.

Thousands of years ago, inhabitants of the Americas learned such a lesson. King Benjamin, a prophet of God, called them to rely upon the Lord and live his commandments: "They all cried with one voice, saying: Yea, we believe all the words which thou hast spoken unto us; and also, we know of their surety and truth, because of the Spirit of the Lord Omnipotent, which has wrought a mighty change in us, or in our hearts, that we have no more disposition to do evil, but to do good continually. . . . And we are willing to enter into a covenant with our God to do his will, and to be obedient to his commandments in all things that he shall command us, all the remainder of our days" (Mosiah 5:2,5).

Individual reliance upon God is the way. British philosopher C. S. Lewis reminded us: "[God] has infinite attention to spare for each one of us. He does not have to deal with us in the mass. You are as much alone with Him as if you were the only being He had ever created. When Christ died, He died for you individually just as much as if you had been the only man [or woman] in the world" (Mere Christianity [1943], 131).

Many people have found that illnesses, both mental and physical, can be benefited or cured by calling upon God. Unfortunately, some people feel that their failure to achieve that remediation and help indicates that God is punishing them or that he isn't even there. Such an attitude is regrettable because it confounds the rebuilding process of body and mind.

Those who are patient and pursue supplication with the Almighty, reach a peace of mind independent of whether or not a cure is accomplished. Some have not found this peace of mind. Those who are angry at the source of their difficulty, trauma or abnormality, or at other individuals, stunt the ability of forgiveness to take hold. Only supplication to God with faith in him and forgiveness of others will bring healing to the mind, body and soul.

Of the many therapeutic initiatives available, I draw attention to the addiction recovery program sponsored by the Church of Jesus Christ of Latter-day Saints. A guide to addiction, recovery and healing, written to support Church leaders and counseling professionals, this program was developed by those who have suffered from addiction and experienced the miracles of recovery through the Atonement of Jesus Christ.

Just as the Lord healed the blind, the lepers, the crippled and the errant, he can heal those who come unto him with repentant hearts.

This program, instituted by LDS Family Services, utilizes the basic twelve-step program so useful with those who have alcohol and drug addiction disorders. An adaptation of the twelve steps draws on a frame of reference typical to the doctrines of the LDS Church. This therapy points to the "mighty change" that can take place in the lives of individuals with addictions. The program is oriented to both those troubled by substance abuse as well as those with behavioral addictions such as pornography. Participants understand the damage done to the brain and other parts of the body as a result of their addictions. The program starts them on the therapeutic process to a life of recovery.

The major changes required for true healing are achieved by the formation of additional dendrites from nerve cells in all three portions of the brain—the prefrontal cortex with its conscience and freedom; the limbic system with its ability to reinforce high degrees of either pleasure or joy; and the basal ganglia, which is not only a source of stimulation for the four basic drives of fundamental brain functioning, but is also responsible for the chronic anxiety that results from substance abuse and addictive behaviors. Nerve cells in all three areas of the brain put out extra connections as illustrated in earlier chapters.

In the prefrontal cortex, the new outcroppings of dendrites from an individual nerve cell can number as many as 185,000. That figure can be increased as a result of the formation of additional dendrites carrying with them the abnormal and excess release of the chemical dopamine, which enhances the pleasure centers of the brain or the basal ganglia with its primitive basilar types of indulgent experiences. To reverse such dendrites is difficult. The therapeutic process requires a combination of spiritual, psychological and socially supportive services from family, as well as from professionals.

While a well-applied therapeutic program can recapture those cells available for recovery, in some cases, major changes within the brain do not allow for rehabilitation. And some brain cells may be lost to the point of being self-destructive.

The brain responds to all types of addiction in a similar manner. The addicted brain becomes selfish and self-centered and unable to grasp what once was easy understanding. These effects are widespread and may take decades to reveal the damage. People whose parents took illicit substances have a greater chance of developing both physical and psychological difficulties, which will have an impact on the fabric of society as measured by education, employment and socioeconomic levels in the population, not to mention the pure human cost in fractured relationships and broken dreams.

One of the most important functions of the brain is sending, receiving and interpreting psychological and behavioral messages. The behavioral sciences refer to these messages as "psychosocial cues." They are sent by language—both body and speech. For example, facial expressions can say much about what someone is thinking. To a great extent, psychosocial cues are a reflection of behavior patterns rather than direct language between ourselves and others.

Communication is driven by cues. Language alone is not enough. For example, in family relations parents and children relate to each other by noticing how family members stand, gesture, smile—or even leave the room.

Alcoholism, drug and tobacco use limit the signals of psychosocial cues. In their own way, each leads to behavioral deficits in understanding and relating to others.

Scientists worldwide are shifting their thinking about the effects of these substances on the brain. In the past, most scientists focused on the function of perceiving what we see and hear without gauging the effect of the substances on the prefrontal lobe functions. They now realize that even the most simple social cues are manipulated by addictions. Conscience, spirituality and decision making are cast aside as the basal ganglia takes over. Relationships and social cues are the casualties.

The effect tends to carry on for multiple generations with statistics to support this extension. While about 12.5 percent of the population is prone to become dependent on alcohol or illicit drugs, those from parents with addictions boost the number to 34 percent.

What does this mean for clinical care?

Aside from the staggering cost to society, the phenomenon of addictive disorders has many implications for clinical psychiatry since addictive behaviors can affect both internally perceived mental states, such as mood, and externally observable activities, such as behavior.

The ramifications are astonishing. Addictions can cause neuropsychiatric symptoms indistinguishable from those of common psychiatric disorders with no known causes (for example, schizophrenia and mood disorders), and thus, primary psychiatric disorders and disorders involving addictive dependency, whether physiological or social problems, are related.

Thus, depression symptoms seen in some people who have not taken a brain-altering substance are indistinguishable from the depression symptoms in a person who has a brain-altering pattern of addiction. There is a brain-based commonality between addictive disorders and depression. Information accumulated over the past decade from those with addictions has shown not only an actual alteration of the nucleus of nerve cells in the brain, but an additional alteration of the DNA genetic make-up of the nerve cells.

Brain imagery shows darkness where light once was.

Through remarkable new techniques of brain imagery, called functional MRI scans or computerized electroencephalography utilizing the newly advanced magneto-EEG, one can observe the adverse effects of all types of addiction, not only those from substance abuse and dependency, but also from behavioral addictive disorders as well. Neuroimagery can reveal the extent to which the brain has undergone fixed changes in terms of loss of frontal and prefrontal tissue, and can verify the direct adverse genetic and environmental contributions to the patient's behavioral problems which may reach major proportions. This neuroimagery can reveal developed, profound disturbances of social conduct and the influences upon the moral and value reasoning area of the prefrontal cortex. Such changes can be seen either from drug use or from behavioral addictions. The result is an impairment of social and moral behaviors.

This impairment comes about as the limbic system and the basal ganglia intensify their activity. The level of anxiety in the nerve circuits also intensifies until the drug or the behavior is repeated. Intense stress and anxiety result in varying degrees of intolerance to the newly combined and abdicated role of limbic and basal ganglia dominance. These nerve cell adaptations underlie behavioral addictive disorders. The rewarding effects of psychomotor-stimulating drugs or behaviors are mediated by the limbic dopamine system. In particular, the projections from dopamine-containing cells that have subsequently developed in all of the pathways of the brain, including the alarming effect of the prefrontal cortex cells, actually put out new dendrites creating dopamine.

As a result, behavioral disorders of an addictive nature can also lead to paranoid psychosis. Illicit drugs and behaviors actually change the structure of neurons in the frontal cortex. Some abnormal substances or behaviors carry with them characteristic changes and manifestations of the addictive disorder. For example, after smoking a cigarette, the prefrontal cortex of the brain, as well as the area of sensory perception tends to shut down and can be marked with deadening or diminution of the function of the prefrontal cortex of the brain. Ordinarily there is a bright neuroimage from normal stimulation of the prefrontal cortex of a non-addicted brain. An abused brain shows a dull and darkened image, indicating low activity.

Let's examine marijuana usage. Because it is slower acting in terms of the development of its addictive dependency, marijuana is considered less serious than the opiates and the psychomotor stimulants such as cocaine, heroin, and methamphetamine. The slow changes of marijuana usage actually destroy brain tissue to a more extensive degree than the other substances, resulting in a permanent loss of tissue which is very difficult to treat once the addictive pattern has reached an intensive level.

Marijuana is called the careless drug because it lessens the capacity of the individual to care. The tragic state of full addictive status is even called "burnout" by drug abusers themselves. Unlike cocaine, which often brings users quickly to their knees, marijuana claims its victims in a slow, cruel fashion. It robs them of their desire to grow or improve, often making heavy users settle for what is left over in life. Its affects are indeed profound, yet subtle. Marijuana smokers rarely come for treatment of their addiction simply because neither they nor their families can feel or differentiate the true individual so damaged by drug use. They commonly sink lower and lower in their performance and in their goals in life and as their pot smoking continues, their lives literally go up in smoke.

Like its cousin marijuana, cannabis can cause severe brain damage over the long term. After six months of use, the damage is measurable by brain imaging. After one year of usage twice weekly, the effects are permanent. This is particularly true of the crystalline form of cannabis.

Those addicted to drugs now dominate 98 percent of admissions to mental health facilities—from private schools to residential treatment units numbering in the thousands across the country.

Binge drinking on college campuses has become epidemic with more than 40 percent indulging on weekends. Universities are recognizing that prolonged usage causes brain damage, and, as a result, a reduction in academic performance. Some 12 percent of our youth are flunking or dropping out of their academic pursuit. Losing their drive to perform and their initiative to make wise choices, these students set aside their occupational and professional goals.

What is clear is that drug usage and substance addictions come first. Depression, anxiety and other mental illnesses follow.

Alteration of Brain Pathways
Characteristic of Addictive Abnormalities

A brief summary of the neurophysiology and the biopsychiatric basis for addictive disorders is revealing. As mentioned previously, unique to the human is an advanced prefrontal cortex. This is a part of the frontal lobe of the brain and collectively constitutes approximately 35 percent of the whole brain structure. The function of the prefrontal cortex of the brain is unique to humans and is not an area or function found within the brains of any animals.

The prefrontal cortex has a separate and unique function in the right hemisphere of the brain as compared with the prefrontal cortex on the left side of the brain. The right hemisphere focuses on morals and values determination. All thoughts that are processed through the various parts of the nervous system come eventually to the right prefrontal cortex for moral and value determination as well as conscience formation.

The prefrontal cortex is the final point to which all information is relayed in order to carry out behavioral decisions or actions. The left prefrontal cortex of the brain allows for the individual to analyze the thought process and engage in what is called by psychologists, inner speech. Under normal circumstances, inner speech allows for the free determination of what we call executive function. Information is then relayed from the prefrontal cortex to various parts of the brain in order to carry out the purpose of the thought and its associated actions.

The relationship between the prefrontal cortex and the limbic system can bring a fullness of joy, a feeling of ecstasy, well-being, and all of the pleasures that characterize man over the animal world. The characteristics of this functioning, as well as other aspects of the role of the prefrontal cortex, involve combinations of conscience and freedom of choice — that which we also call agency.

The limbic system under certain circumstances, however, can relate primarily to the basal ganglia or primitive aspects of the nervous system at the base of the brain. This particular relationship often results in the development of patterns which result in addictive disorders.

To bring about this change of neurological functioning, a change must take place within the nucleus of the nerve cells of the nervous system within the prefrontal cortex, and in severe cases an alteration of the nerve cells in the basal ganglia. There is not only a rearrangement of the electrical functioning of each nerve cell or neuron, which performs a singular and specific function, but an interrelation between those nerve cells and other aspects of the brain that can often elicit severe nerve pathways and different functions of neurons.

Very serious, however, is the actual change of DNA, the chemical and genetic determination found within the chromosomes or nucleus of the nerve cell. Unless this change is dealt with, it can become permanent.

Chapter 4

Turmoil in the Adolescent Brain

"Warn them that are unruly . . . hold fast that which is good."

—*1 Thes. 5:14, 21*

I<small>N EVERY GENERATION THE SAME LAMENT IS EXPRESSED</small> by parents of teenagers: "What is the matter with kids today?" "Why are they so confused, annoying, demanding, moody, defiant, and reckless?"

Adolescents ask the reverse: "What is the matter with the older generation?" "Why are they so old-fashioned, so boring, so out-of-touch?"

Incompatible? Not really. But, both may be locked in place.

When so many parents are sincerely seeking to raise their children in righteousness, why do we have this battle for the minds—and hence, souls—of our children? Because the mind is disconnecting from its God-given role at an alarming rate. Self-medication—the soft-sell name for addiction in all its abhorrent forms—is the growing answer to the life they have been handed. Ahead is a slow death of betrayal, rage, hopelessness, lost opportunity, and broken dreams. Recent studies indicate that the dominant influences on youth in our society today include popular music, movies, television, books, politicians, polls and, yes, parents. But religion, God, and spiritual strength do not even make the top ten.

There's no question that accidental deaths, suicides, homicides, indulgence in sex, drugs and violence are more intense today than in generations past. Today's youth are experiencing a world where psychosis, major depression, addictions and eating disorders are common. The very culture of society is changing. Everyday unhappiness reaches its peak in the teens.

Adolescents feel the need to assert their independence and explore limits, take risks, break rules, and rebel against their parents while still relying on them for support and protection. In many ways their lives are a mixed bag.

Behavioral science research has identified that such unsettled moods and behavior may be rooted in uneven brain development. The question is not intellectual maturity. Science has found that abstract reasoning, memory and judgment can often be repressed by negative behavior. The conscience, moral and value discernment, and appropriate decision making can be set aside by "acting out."

It is a normal, positive process for growth and development of the prefrontal cortex to take place during adolescence, reaching full development by mid teens. As teens confront issues and hypothetical questions of risk and reward, they are prone to give the same expected answers as results. But the emotional state in which they confront those questions is not necessarily one in which they actually make wise and appropriate choices. They may find it far more difficult to interrupt an action underway, to think before acting or even to choose between safe and more risky alternatives. For example, it is easy for them to say they would not get into a car with a drunk driver, but more difficult to turn down an invitation when confronted with that option in the company of peers. Teen judgment can be overwhelmed by the urge for new experiences, thrill seeking, or sexual and aggressive impulses. They sometimes seem driven to seek experiences merely for the strong feelings and sensations.

Social pressure is their blind spot. Much of their troubling behavior occurs in groups where peer pressure is at work. Such influence is capable of distracting or redirecting even the "best" teenage brain, turning youth toward behaviors with seriously negative consequences. The choices of adults correspond well to their reasoning in such a setting; for teens the correlation is weaker.

The differences are found in the brain structure and function. Research shows that human brain circuitry is not fully mature until the early twenties. The last connections to be established are the links between the seat of moral and value judgment (the prefrontal cortex), and the emotional centers (the limbic system), and especially the amygdala. These links are essential for higher level thinking, experiencing and self-regulation.

Here's how it works. The limbic system is made up of distinct parts which connect with the prefrontal cortex of the brain. (See Figure 3.) The limbic area also connects with the basal ganglia, which serve the brain as the trigger for an alarm if there is danger.

Here's where the disparity between an adolescent's stepping into a foolish adventure and an adult's sensible retreat becomes obvious. Brain circuits are still under construction in adolescents, which is why most addicts get their start during the teenage years. Studies

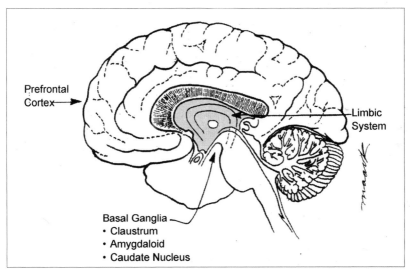

Figure 3. The limbic system is the emotional part of the brain. In a healthy state it serves the prefrontal cortex. It can also negatively serve the basal ganglia of the brain with its primitive, animal-like instincts.

have found that adolescents become addicted to nicotine and other drugs faster and at lower doses. Functional brain scans suggest that teenagers and adults process reward stimuli differently; adolescents are hypersensitive to the value of the novel experience.

Hormonal changes are at work too. The adolescent brain pours out adrenal stress hormones, sex hormones and growth hormones which in turn influence brain development. The production of testosterone increases ten times in adolescent boys. Sex hormones act in the limbic system and in the raphe nucleus, source of the neurotransmitter serotonin, which is important for the regulation of arousal, mood and making appropriate moral decisions. The hormonally regulated 24-hour clocks change their settings during adolescence, keeping high school and college students awake far into the night and making it difficult to rise for morning classes.

As long as the brain is still in formation, things can go wrong in many ways and some of them involve the onset of psychiatric disorders. Stress can restart the growth of the hippocampus, which consolidates memories. The pruning of gray matter and the development of connections between nerve cells in the frontal and prefrontal lobe areas can give rise to increasing susceptibility to psychiatric disorders. The failure of optimal growth and development, particularly in the prefrontal cortex, makes the adolescent more vulnerable to the early symptoms of depression and even schizophrenia.

New research stereotypes adolescents and provides a biological explanation for irresponsible behavior. The development of the human brain does not unfold automatically and uniformly. There is much individual variation that reflects experience, as well as gene programming. The problems of teenagers are not all in their brains, but have many causes—social, individual, genetic, and environmental. At present and probably far into the future, researchers will be gathering better information on the mental and emotional development of adolescents. For the most part, these have come about, and will continue to unfold, through behavioral and psychological testing rather than from brain scans alone.

Neuroscience research is becoming more sophisticated. Already, long-term studies are following subjects through frequent periodic psychological testing as well as through brain scans over the course of their lives. The results will demonstrate the effects of behavioral and cognitive therapies on psychiatric illnesses that we commonly find among misdirected and disturbed adolescents.

Can medications for psychiatric disorders trigger suicide?

Psychiatric disorders can be treated with medications. Does such treatment increase the chance of suicide? Suicidal thoughts (although no suicides) have been reported in people taking selective serotonin reuptake inhibitors (SSRIs). (See Figure 4). In 1990, shortly after the medications were introduced, the FDA rejected the association of

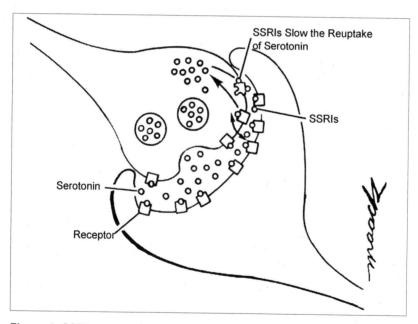

Figure 4. SSRIs are used to treat depression and assist the frontal/prefrontal cortex of the brain to become normally active. They do this by retaining a plentiful supply of the chemical serotonin at the nerve junction and preventing an abnormal reuptake of serotonin. Antidepressants are therefore called selective serotonin reuptake inhibitors.

SSRIs with suicide and most mental health professionals accept the FDA's conclusion; but, until recently the issue was not fully resolved.

The debate circled around an increase in the number of children and adolescents receiving prescriptions for anxiety and depression as well as bipolar disorder. Other problems stem from eating disorders or depressive complications associated with attention deficit disorders. In 2003, authorities announced a possible connection between SSRIs and thoughts of suicide or self-harm in children and adolescents. Universities, the National Institute of Mental Health, and the Food and Drug Administration all made thorough studies in 2004 and 2005.

A consistent trend emerged. Antidepressants, including SSRI compounds, seemed to double the risk of suicidal thinking during the first six weeks of therapy. The increase went from 1.2 percent to 2.4 percent in both children and adults in the first six weeks of being medicated. None of the studies, however, reported any cases of actual suicide. So far, there is no evidence from controlled research that links suicide to antidepressant use.

Depression itself increases the risk of suicide and is common in adolescents. Mental health scientists have found that depressed people recover energy and awareness during the first few weeks of therapy before the medications reach full effectiveness. A few, however, develop suicidal thoughts before their mood improves or hope returns. Psychiatrists are very careful in prescribing antidepressants to those with bipolar disorder because the medication may trigger mania or irritability, hence, increasing the risk of self-destructive thoughts.

Regular or frequent follow-up during the first six to eight weeks by a psychiatrist or other physician can eliminate the risk of suicide. If, after beginning treatment, a person develops uncomfortable symptoms in the first few weeks, the doctor should be notified. The same advice holds true for children and teenagers. Researchers have determined that after the first six weeks of medication, the small incidence of suicide actually lessens as compared with the general population who do not have mental illness.

What does it take to get a teen back on track?

Research has found pronounced importance in the support of family during an adolescent's growth and development. The studies find that the family, as a teaching and training institution, is fundamental. Observation of parents by their adolescents, and the example set by these parents, can be the best model for teen learning.

The best treatment for psychiatric illness is preventive. Optimal communication in families is the key. Parents who establish good communication with their children from the time they are toddlers and on up, have the easiest time communicating with their adolescents.

The influence of peer groups is also fundamental. Peer experiences supported by church groups, clubs, and positive social organizations contribute to the optimal development of a happy adolescent.

Studies clearly show that treatment of parents and youth together is essential. Some teens will require psychotherapy, either on an individual or group basis and some will need to be assisted through residential psychiatric treatment centers. Group therapy with peers is equally helpful. Both have the instruments for guiding the adolescent back into a more optimal pattern of growth and development. Positive peer culture therapy also allows the adolescent, as he or she evolves through the curative process and rehabilitation, the opportunity of service to subsequent peers in the remediation of their challenges. This process of giving and sharing has been found to be a chief way of circumventing the self-centered operation of negative adolescent behavior.

Chapter 5

The Brain Believes
What You Tell It

"Say to them that are of a fearful heart, Be strong."

—*Isaiah 35:4*

MAN IS THAT HE MIGHT HAVE JOY" is not a platitude of someday, somewhere, some time. Joy is a "heart condition" that is manifested by the brain. It is the imprinting of vitality and fulfillment and mastery on the brain.

Imagine a life that does not give in to the barriers, hassles and hurdles of everyday living. One filled with achievement, enrichment, self-fulfillment and satisfaction. One that can sustain light in a world that is "walking in darkness at noonday." Mastering the mind is the key to that light. A brain that has been imprinted with negative thoughts, patterns and processes can be reconnected to the truth and future it has lost.

The human brain is capable of doing anything we would like it to do. But we have to know how to use it and how to treat it. What we imprint determines what we see, feel, do and like. If we treat the brain carefully, giving it the right direction, it will do the right thing and work for us in the right way as God intended. But if we give our highly sophisticated brain the wrong directions, those imprints will develop negative programs that "dumb-down" our potential. For example, those who are addicted, feel and think of nothing but feeding their need; those who have lived with violence and abuse see no other way to survive. Negative imprints dominate our society.

But the brains of our youth are still in the developmental stage. Not only are teens all legs one day, and arms and ears the next, the regions of their brains are being developed as well. Their brains are at work learning how to balance the emotional center of the brain with the judgment of the prefrontal cortex. A majority of youth are imprinting their brains with negative programs of worldliness and its evils that are not reality. Yet wrong thinking programs their brains—and ours—year after year, word by word, until our scripts are etched, or imprinted, with society's ills as if they were what we came to do. So many of our youth are living out the "wrong" picture of themselves that has been created in their minds. Unfortunately, so are many of their parents.

The result is a disconnect from our eternal selves. But negative programming can be erased—just like a disk in a computer—and replaced with positive programming that will stay with us and drive our thinking, our feelings and our actions.

Work in Progress

The brain inside a teen is still a work in progress. Being put in place are the connections between neurons, the transmitters that join not only emotional skills but also physical and mental abilities. In the past, society simply tried to pack a teen's brain with facts and figures—from the War of 1812 to the hypotenuse of a triangle to how to jump-start a car. And in the process of educating, the teen was "done."

Times and understanding have changed. Studies of the brain show that the brain through adolescence is maturing in fits and starts. Raw emotions surface only to be played back by judgment and empathy. This imbalance is a reflection of imprints not yet cohesive. In scientific terms, this means neurons or brain cells are "firing" to dendrites of another brain cell. Moodiness and incoherent behavior are almost standard. That's why a teen will pop into a car too crowded for seat belts, or worse, being driven by someone who is high on drugs. The same teen will comfort a child and feel intense emotion for a lost puppy.

It is clear that the brain is an incredibly complex physiological mechanism and that the internal structure of the brain is uniquely human. To review, the prefrontal cortex is the portion that differentiates us from the animal world, and allows us to make judgments, to process all other brain functions and bring balance to our thinking. The limbic system and basal ganglia are centers that initiate emotions. The limbic system can either enhance the functions of the prefrontal cortex or act independently with the more primitive basal ganglia that promote and sustain bad habits.

Within the brain itself, a network of 200 billion neurons, each having a potential of 185,000 electrochemical switches called neurotransmitters, turns part of us on and part of us off. The brain's infinitely small chemical receiving centers respond to almost imperceptible electrochemical signals which deliver nearly immeasurable but highly potent chemical substances to our brain and to other organs which in turn control or affect everything we do.

Programmed by Thoughts

Through the joint effort of body, brain and mind, we become the living results of our own thoughts. Every action we take, of any kind, is affected by prior programming—imprinting. A positive set of attitudes, beliefs and behaviors prompts an abundance of self-belief and the moral foundation for our life's direction. The same is true for established patterns that follow the darker side of society. Hence, the prefrontal cortex is what scientists call the "executive" portion of the brain. This area dictates the positive development of the person. In contrast, the more primitive and self-indulgent parts of the brain can take over and dictate negative addictive behaviors where no freedom of choice is available.

Fortunately, there is always a programming vocabulary or "inner speech" that can be used to erase and replace the negative imprinting or programming with positive, productive new directions. That inner speech is a singularly human endowment that can be activated or reactivated at any time.

Put simply, the brain believes what *you* tell it most. What you tell it about you—what you like, what you do, what you want, what you need—will create you as your brain sees it. It is what neuroscientists have defined as a "brain-soul" combination manifest by what might be called "inner speech."

The location and function of inner speech (what we say to ourselves) is found in the prefrontal cortex of the brain. This exercise of free agency or choice, not found in animals, allows us to make moral and value judgments in one part of the prefrontal lobes of the brain and in another location prompts us to exercise our ability to carry on an inner speech or dialogue pattern. That inner speech is the ingredient that binds all other elements in our process of self-fulfillment.

Chapter 6

Pornography:
Molesting the Minds of Our Youth

". . .and from the roof he saw a woman washing herself:
and the woman was very beautiful to look upon."

—*2 Samuel 11:2*

TIME WAS WHEN SODOM AND GOMORRAH was considered as bad as it could get. The entire civilization was consumed by sex in all its forms and fashions.

Today's society is spinning downward into a similar culture of bizarre mindsets, beliefs and practices. Sex is paraded about like an ice cream truck on a Saturday afternoon. And the result is being recorded—we call it imprinting—on the brains of the young.

President Gordon B. Hinckley stated in a 2004 leadership training broadcast, "I do not know that things were worse in the times of Sodom and Gomorrah."

Sobering.

Pornography is the heart of sexual perversion. It is everywhere. Condoned as "free speech," it looks nothing like what the Founding Fathers had in mind. All boundaries and taboos have been dropped; anything goes as long as it is pleasure-driven. Hollywood, with its misguided pop culture, is fanning the flames. What once was considered intimate and even honored, is now ever-present, cheap, meaningless and tawdry and it is available for the young.

Immaturity of the teenage brain makes it vulnerable to miscues or misdirections. Imprinted with pornography, the brain rewires to the new stimulation as if this were the course for a lifetime. Developing the ability to plan, organize, manage emotions, understand others, read circumstances, and exercise judgment are pushed aside by the need to feel exhilarated by sexual stimulation, and that is trouble.

Put simply, the massive imprinting of sex in today's culture is prompting an addiction that has swept at least 30% of the male population and is growing among women as well. Some statistics say it is as high as one out of two churchgoers in this country.

Magazines which were once the domain for pornography, with their centerfold titillations, were kept behind the counter. It was a "don't ask, don't tell" mentality. Times have changed. Sex has jumped to the Internet with a vengeance and taken hold of unsuspecting minds by the hundreds of thousands. Because of a strong and natural human sex drive, all it takes is one view, no more than four, to be imprinted and possibly addicted—for life.

Pornography addiction is characterized by obsessive viewing, reading, and thinking about pornographic images or sexual themes to the detriment of other uplifting elements of life.

The recent scientific breakthrough of neural imagery from magnetic resonance scans show significant slowing of prefrontal lobe function. With pornography use, emotional "colored" messages are sent to the prefrontal area of the brain for value judgment and decision making. In a state of alarm, the brain transmission is immediate, as the basal ganglia and limbic system have done their jobs putting into place a sophisticated and complex response system. Until the emergency is resolved, the prefrontal cortex remains in a state of anxiety. This prolonged state of anxiety within the prefrontal cortex leads to the destruction of brain cells, which are difficult to replace and correct. Such loss in all addictions makes it more difficult to repent. They at times reach the point of requiring a "mighty change" to alter the problem and the remediation of addictive disorder.

Faith-based organizations are recognizing and responding to the growing evil. The high number involved in pornography, as compared with drug users, is catching everyone's attention. The Church of Jesus Christ of Latter-day Saints reports that 25 percent of male members have some level of involvement with pornography.

With the growth of online pornography, every imaginable sexual experience has been spread across the screens of America and has been shoved into the faces of many whose emails are clogged with hardcore sexual images. It's done in secret, hidden in the minds of the users. An added concern is the rationalization that there is nothing wrong with pornography since there is no "acting out."

What is the result? Viewers want more. Not because they are bad people, or because they have sought sex, but because they have had one glance imprinted, and for many that is all it took. Whatever dark and loathsome activity you can imagine, someone out there is actually putting it on the Internet, drawing others to their harmful thinking. It is destroying our society.

Current research indicates that pornography addicts experience similar patterns of symptoms to those involved in physiological addiction to substances such as drugs and alcohol. For example, euphoria while viewing pornography stimulates the need to increase the exposure in order to sustain the euphoria-producing effects. Much like drug addiction, it demands more and more viewing to simply maintain the "high."

Unlike other addictions, however, pornography has several prongs that reinforce behavior. This addiction not only creates a mental "high" in the brain, it also stimulates the body physically and emotionally to indulge in perverse sexual behavior and blocks normal sexual relationships in future marriage.

In the pornography-addicted brain, the viewing of such intense graphic, physiological and emotional material imprints the brain with images driven straight to the basal ganglia where feeling is stored. Euphoria! For a moment. The initial experience produces feel-good sensations but what follows is irritability, anxiety, distress and even despair until the next experience. And the next. It is compelling to know that each "session" produces a high, but never one equal to the first.

Adolescent indulgence leads to rejection of religious doctrines and family-oriented relationships, both present and future. These impressionable youth, drawn into pornography, experience time distortion. Time can pass without any conceptualization of life outside the moment.

It is astonishing that today's popular culture—from gender confusion to perverse sexual expression—has lost its Christian values and debunks any efforts to hold the line at virtue and morality. Even the very mention of the words "virtue" or "morality" bring jeers and charges of being "old-fashioned."

In past eras, parents had the rest of society to help with the fight between good and evil. Youth could bond to teachers, church leaders, mentors or other organizations for healthy direction and for affirmation of their parents' beliefs. But today, youth have been cut loose, drawn off in an iPod world that puts cell phones at their fingertips and parental guidance at arm's length.

In summary, the effects of pornography addiction are dramatic and disturbing. They further degrade society, family, and personal integrity while focusing on self-centered, aberrant behavior.

Symptoms of the normalization of adverse reactions to offensive material:

1. Developing tolerance and a need for more novel or bizarre material to achieve the same arousal.
2. Mistakenly perceiving sexual activity as exaggerated in the general populous.
3. Overestimating the prevalence of less common sexual practices.
4. Abandoning the idea of exclusive fidelity.
5. Perceiving promiscuity as a normal state of interaction.
6. Developing cynical attitudes about love.
7. Believing superior sexual satisfaction is obtainable without affection from one's partner.
8. Believing marriage is sexually confining.

9. Developing a negative body image about women.
10. Believing that family and marriage are an unattractive prospect.
11. Increasing risk for developing sexual compulsions.
12. Increasing risk for developing sexual addiction.
13. Increasing risk for believing incorrect information about human sexual behavior.

Who are these people molesting the minds of our youth?

Child pornography is a big business operated by perverted people. They are addicted not only to their own distorted sexual fantasies but to the money generated by rolling out one pornographic image after another. The porn industry claims to haul in more than $57 billion a year.

"Somebody is watching. Somebody likes this. Somebody thinks it is okay," one proclaimed transvestite, a porn producer said to me. "What we know," he continued, "is that we get a lot of money."

One of the chief porn producers in the country boasts that he owns almost 3,000 different domains in which probably 80 percent of them are adult domains and about 20 percent for children. He provides a safeguard with a warning page on all websites. The effort is as effective as the half-hearted statement on a pack of cigarettes, "Smoking may be hazardous to your health."

This "businessman," as he calls himself, has justified his livelihood stating, "You know it is not my job to tell the public that your kid comes home early from school or to tell you what he is doing. He is going to your computer and he is looking at pornography. It is not my job to tell you."

An ex-porn star explained, "My mom molested me at age eleven and this sent me into a tailspin that lasted until I was 35 years old. As a child, she also exposed me to pornography. What do you think of a child who is exposed to pornography as well as sexual molestation and ends up having the same line of thinking? What would stop that kid from being sent into a tailspin? This led me to my addiction to pornography."

Sad stories accompany every account of those drawn into and obsessed by pornography. One is a young woman I call Shelley. She describes, "When I was nine years old I had a classmate that asked me to spend the night. I trusted her. Her older brother was really cute and I loved it when he paid attention to me. So that night he asked me if I wanted to go skinny dipping and I didn't know what skinny dipping meant. He asked me to come to the pool and he came behind me and pulled my bikini bottoms down and he started touching me in my genitals. I just remember being frozen at that moment. I was exposed to something that was totally sick and it made me sick. You just think this is very bad. The next morning I ran away so fast from that house. I didn't even stay for breakfast or say goodbye. I was so full of shame; I couldn't believe what had been done to me."

Her encounter is a reminder to us all. The young and developing brain is not prepared to handle early sexual experiences. She told no one, not even her parents. She continues, "Three years following this tragic and imprinting experience, I started sleeping with some of the boys in the neighborhood and got a reputation as the school slut. I had had outbursts of rage where I would want to act out sexually and I would just push it back down. I believe when teenagers or children are exposed to either pornography or sexual trauma at a young age, they do not know what to do with it. Who are they going to tell? There is no one to tell. They are these silent victims who have to hold it in, but it is there. It becomes a very tangible substance. A very real trauma that they live with daily and they become merely survivors rather than thriving."

At age 14, short on money for drugs, she went to work for a porn photographer. Her pay was $35 a day. Her first impression of the place was "deep evil" but when encouraged to drink some whiskey, she soon dismissed the apprehension. The place was filthy with feces piled on the floor. Dancing nude for the camera, she allowed men to commit perverse sexual acts. The imprints were deep and destructive. She continued, however, being encouraged with "two lines of cocaine" before indulging in the day's activities.

She later shifted to prostitution and by age 18 was pregnant. Still needing financial support she became a nude dancer in a club until the baby was born.

Shelley's experience is not unique. It graphically describes the desperation that replaces reason. The imprinting began young but Shelley was not lost. A group of young adults befriended her and over a two-year period she was converted to the gospel of Jesus Christ. Her trust grew in those whose path had been so foreign to her own and she married one of the group. She described her new life as one of intense peace, a feeling she had never known before. Christ had brought about a "mighty change" in her.

Pornographers see nothing wrong with what they are doing and hide behind "free speech." Such a twisted approach to a sacred trust has deep roots in this country and many others around the world.

An interview with the executive director of a coalition whose sole purpose is to promote pornography under the guise of the constitutional guarantee of "free speech" is stunning. "There are actually a lot of very positive outcomes that the consumption of adult entertainment can have for people," she justified to me. "Marital aid. It can help people heal from sexual assaults. It can help people that have a physical dysfunction. It improves their sex life."

Nothing could be further from the truth. No such claims can be substantiated by those who have studied pornography.

She continued, "If religious people really wanted to change things, they would focus on positive, proactive things they could do to change people's lives. They should not be concerned about pornography addictions as one of those causes."

Even the general counsel for the coalition claimed, "There has never been a study anywhere in the literature which showed there is harm for a 7-year-old, or a 14-year-old, or a 17-year-old looking at sexually explicit material called, by you, pornography."

Damage *has* been documented; the damage is real. They and others of their ilk should talk with Paul, a young man who is recovering from addiction to pornography. He said, "The other drugs such as marijuana, cocaine and methamphetamine, they will eventully just leave your body, but the pornography images will stay in your head for a long, long time."

The purveyors of porn continue to seek new venues for marketing their damaged goods. Right now, pornography on the Internet is the door into the minds of our youth. Filters are no protectors. Schools have had to shut down computer systems because of crafty and clever hacking into the controls, allowing access to pornographic sites. Next, the porn industry has targeted cell phones. The escalation continues to rip apart our society.

What to do?

Be virtuous. Consider your imprint on the minds of your youth. If you live according to the rules you have set, honestly seeking to do the right thing at the right time, to act with integrity, to present the best in you, though you are far from perfect, you will create, form and shape an image for your youth to consider. Youth need patience, firmness, limits, kindness, insight and honest, not hypocritical, examples. In other words, they need to feel genuine parental love and direction. It comes from constancy and integrity to a cause greater than today and tomorrow.

That does not suggest imposing limits and rules that speak louder than your love. It means being reasonable and accessible. Otherwise, they will resent your structure—and you. And that rage will manifest itself in complex and evil ways. Children feel compelled to rebel against authority when you fail them. Everything forbidden—from sex to drugs to tattoos—speaks of personal freedom from you. Practices they once would have shunned or even ignored become enticing, and then just one experience imprints their minds. Next the basal area of the brain begins to drive their decisions, their addictions.

Take pornography seriously. Expect that every youth has been or will be exposed to pornographic images. Talk with them about the degradation of such imagery, the risks of losing their own will to basal needs. Keep them talking to you day after day, week after week and help them fill their "down time" with something that stimulates their creative senses, their athletic interests, or their social skills. Be there for those activities and those quiet moments.

Pornography is accessed behind closed doors. It is harsh and dirty—and inescapable. Youth are not prepared to fight it alone. They need support to supplant that addiction with other stimuli. They need intervention. Parents must continue to love them, to help them turn off the monitor and never to return.

You have heard the advice to put the computer in the middle of a room, not in their room or the basement. However, it takes more than placement of the machine because your child's friend's laptop can bring up those images so quickly. Help your children prepare responses and ways to get out of uncomfortable settings without losing face. They need personal will and commitment, spiritual strength and constant check-ups. They need to trust you will be there and if you are that rock of constancy, they can reverse that imprinting.

Be realistic. In most households, youth are far more savvy about accessing sites on the computer than parents. For those already caught in the web, the drive to view pornography is so compelling that they violate the family rules; some make excuses for using computers at the homes of friends. One college student used to get up in the middle of the night to use his roommate's computer. Sometimes his sessions—all viewing pornography—lasted for hours. He was finally discovered by his roommate and he admitted he had been addicted since he was 12. His family, aware of his problem, had hoped college would distract him.

Hold a family council and make some determinations that the group can help uphold. Talk one-on-one—not once, but often. Discuss the basic beliefs that pornography promotes:

1. I am basically a bad, unworthy person
2. No one could love me as I am.
3. My needs are never going to be met if I have to depend on others.
4. Sex is my most important need.

These can be reversed with the following shifts in thinking:

1. I am a worthwhile person, deserving of pride.
2. I am loved and accepted by people who know me as I am.
3. My needs can be met by others if I let them know what I need.
4. Sex is but one expression of the needs in a caring marriage.

Find new interests you can share. Work at it together. Be prepared to teach and re-teach the sacred principle of chastity and its blessings.

Become involved as a family in therapy for rehabilitation of the one who suffers. LDS Family Services provides rehabilitation of mental and behavioral problems and offers both individual and group therapies. They understand and apply the power of repentance, forgiveness, and the Lord in the healing process.

Be aware. The denial of repentance abounds in the thinking "imprinted" by pornography.

Act responsibly. In several states throughout the country organizations have been able to put laws in place that are strict and firm. In Utah, multiple cases of arrests for filming and selling child pornography have brought prison terms of 60 to 72 months for the offenders. Sentences of five or six years are at least a beginning. Citizens need to be involved and aggressive in ridding their own communities of the porn industry. National organizations have active committees involving citizens and religious groups—all of which strengthen the movement to attack pornography. Two have partnered to produce a film (see www.trafficcontrolthemovie.com) detailing the hazards of pornography on the Internet. Other Internet sites that may be helpful are www.legacyleader.com and www.livingbiography.com. A board of directors chaired by John Harmer, a nationally recognized community leader, leads a nationwide effort through the Lighted Candle Society. Those interested in this global effort can connect at www.lightedcandlesociety.org or can email lightedcandlesociety@msn.com.

If your area does not have some organization to help shut down child pornography, consider sponsoring one with your local schools, community action groups or churches.

Turn to the Lord. The Spirit can cleanse the soul and erase the images in the mind. Trust that the Spirit of God can reverse the imprints of pornographic addiction and bring healing to a troubled mind. Live worthy of that blessing beginning today.

Chapter 7

The Power to Choose

"Ye are free to act for yourselves."

—*2 Nephi 10:23*

THE CREATOR INSTILLS IN EACH ONE OF US both the desire and the ability to find meaning and joy in life. Yet many, youth in particular, struggle to make sense of the drama of everyday living, to make a place for themselves, to feel of real value and to make a contribution. There is something in each of us that seeks daily to find at least a small positive measure we can add to our storehouse of living. The ingredients for a meaningful life are all around us: good music, a walk on a spring day, prayer and quiet reflection, time with friends.

Yet we see discouragement, despair and destructive behaviors everywhere we turn. The battle is not here-and-now politics. It began during the pre-mortal life, with the War in Heaven, when we fought for the right to choose. It continues today, not in the streets, media and tabloids, but in our minds. Imprinted in the brains of so many is a confused compilation of wrongs that seem right that lead to destructive and abhorrent behavior.

Put simply, our attitudes, ideas, responses and experiences can be exalting. We can counter the wasted living of drugs, sex, violence, suicide, gender confusion, the occult, and abortion, being flaunted as progressive, upscale, upbeat and politically correct.

There is truth to the ancient verse, "As a man thinketh, so is he."

Studies in the past two decades have revealed that by an incredibly complex physiological mechanism—a joint effort of body, brain and mind—we become the living results of our own thoughts. We become what we think about most. What we think about, programs what we say when we engage in inner speech—like talking to ourselves. The brain believes what we tell it most. And what we tell it most about us, it will create. It has choice.

The location and function of inner speech, neuroscientists tell us, is found in the uniquely human prefrontal cortex of the brain. Everything about us—our memory, our judgment, our attitude, our fears, our creativity, logic and spirit—is controlled by the switches in our mental central room. As discussed previously, the brain holds a network of 200 billion neurons, each having the potential of 185,000 electrochemical switches, called neurotransmitters, which turn part of us on and part of us off. The brain's infinitesimally small chemical receiving centers respond to almost imperceptible electrochemical signals which deliver nearly immeasurable but highly potent chemical substances to our brain and to our other organs—which in turn control or affect everything we do.

Whatever thoughts or behaviors you have imprinted yourself, or have allowed others to imprint on your brain, are affecting, directing and controlling everything about you.

Every day each of us receives an endless stream of commands, directives, controls, inducements and expectations from others. Everything around us nudges, demands or persuades. We are met with a torrent of influences, which imprint our brains. Good or bad, they are put in place and they act as directional signs to future behavior.

Most of us juggle positive and negative imprints. Can we override the programs in our minds that work against us, and replace them with refreshing new imprints of true beliefs? Can we undo the shackles of bad habits, old conditioning, and self-doubt? Can the brain be freed—imprinted anew—to self-direct as God intended?

Yes. With inner speech.

Inner speech is a remarkable level of brain functioning found only in the human mind. As long as the prefrontal lobes are performing—unencumbered by addictive patterns—they are directing our conversations within.

With inner speech we give new direction to our minds by talking to ourselves in a different way. We can consciously re-program our prefrontal cortex with words and statements that are more effective and help with improving ourselves and creating new imprints. Inner conversation can paint a new internal picture of us—what we would like to be, we can be. (See Figure 5.)

We can put off the old self and become a different, better self, a self no longer the product of conditioned or addictive responses. We can be governed, anew, by personal freedom of choice. We can activate or reactivate our souls to communicate and receive the influences from Him who gave us our free agency. A "mighty change" is not a hollow promise.

"Negative speak" can plague inner speech. Self-conversation can "speak" to poor acceptance. Negative talk can become a compulsion representing "instructions" from our simplest misgivings, to loss of control of the brain and spirit, to a primitively driven addiction to all types of agency-destroying behavior. In the beginning of negative inner directions there is no way to estimate the amount of havoc and misdirection that such talk wreaks in our lives. It cripples our best intentions and seduces us to become satisfied or compelled to indulge in debased behaviors. Rid yourself of the negative and its evil direction and you rid yourself of your greatest foe.

It takes help from God. We must see ourselves as he sees us, as he talks to us, as he listens. We must see beyond the artificial barriers constructed by living out our days with no spiritual infusion, no strength from the Savior's Atonement.

Our commitment to change must involve confessing or acknowledging to ourselves, and others, regret of past behaviors and the need for change. The inner speech should then move us to the decision to

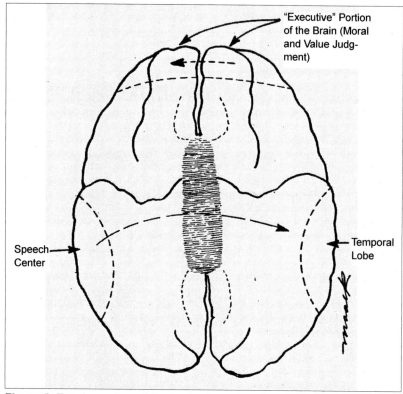

Figure 5. Top-down view of the brain shows how inner speech is processed. New thoughts have their origin in the left hemisphere of the brain where they are formulated into inner speech and then sent to the right hemisphere for emotional "coloring." Next they go to the right prefrontal cortex for moral and value judgment, and finally, they're sent to the left prefrontal cortex for the final decision-making process before an action is initiated.

change and then evolve to the level of faith that you believe there can be a better you. The final level of inner speech is reaching the level of universal affirmation. This level has been spoken for thousands of years. It is as old as the ancient religion that inspired it.

Inner speech can provide "oneness" with God. It can speak of a unity of spirit, a divine and timeless affinity, and, through the love of the Lord, transcends all worldly things and gives meaning to our being.

The concept of positive thinking is a good start. Unfortunately, such help is temporary unless we have programmed our minds to go beyond just condemning the negative. Making a decision to never again think negatively, and for the rest of our lives think positively, while it may work for a time, cannot last. Why? Because the mental imprints still sit deep in our minds. They have to be replaced by new imprints, new ways of seeing and saying things. If we tell ourselves that from today onward we will never again think negatively, without at the same time giving ourselves a specific, new word vocabulary of the positive things to say to ourselves, we will soon slip back to the old habit of thinking negatively.

In order to correct inner speech, you must identify your inner speech. Write down all of the experiences of negative moods, situations, self-labels you use to stereotype and depress yourself. Number how frequently they occur and how often they make you feel guilty, gloomy and pessimistic.

In their place, substitute hopeful written statements and avoid dwelling on past and forgiven problems. Blaming talk that constantly reviews past hurts will keep you experiencing pain, depression and often anger. You may have to command yourself to stop! Then switch your thoughts to a pre-planned more pleasant or even neutral subject. Add images to your mind that are positive for ideas or memory. Reinforce your command by saying to yourself: "These recurring thoughts are making me feel guilty, hurt, angry, anxious, worried and depressed, and I absolutely refuse to continue these downgrading feelings."

Wanting to be a positive thinker is not enough. Making the decision to have a positive attitude is not enough. Your mind says: "Give me more, give me the words, give me the directions, the commands, the picture, the schedule, and the results I want." Where do you go? The answer is to "feast upon the words of Christ" and He will give you the "words." Educate and program your mind by searching the scriptures. Although other methods and other people may be helpful, no one else can replace the "words of Christ." No one else has that right.

Chapter 8

The Hidden Evils
of Anxiety and Stress

"God hath not given us the spirit of fear."

—*2 Tim. 1:7*

I RECENTLY CHUCKLED OVER A NEWSPAPER CARTOON. A zebra, looking back on himself as his stripes fell to the ground, quipped, "I think I'm having stress!" Humorous, but all too poignantly true. All of us at one time or another have fallen apart!

All around us we hear people talk of being "stressed out." Busyness has become the order of the day in this ever-changing, fast-paced world. As 24/7 news programs flash images on the screen at a flick of the remote, media projects images that thrive and survive on evoking chronic tension in the viewer. Stress is, quite simply, a term of our era, like a badge of honor in a culture that feeds on fast and furious.

Where is this stress coming from? Is it a product of childhood neglect or abuse—emotional or sexual? Is it from separation from family, death, conflict at home, or divorce? Is it a source of chronic fear such as a severe illness? All can result in post-traumatic stress disorder.

Tension and worry crescendo as we watch catastrophic events unfold—extreme weather, terrorism, economic downturns, upturns, and overturns, missing children, the traumas and effects of war. All play out on the small screen. Internal tensions caused by marital conflict, parent/child conflict, work issues, and financial difficulties can fuel anxiety. Stress is caused by everyday disappointments, especially when they string together.

In addition, some individuals must deal with the terrible underpinnings associated with physical, emotional, and sexual abuse, deprivation, and personal trauma. Stress and anxiety may haunt those who have inflicted this pain on others. Neglect is an especially harmful childhood stressor. Destructive neglect of a child can be as debilitating as physical, psychological or sexual abuse.

Addictive behaviors are another source of chronic anxiety and stress.

The cycle of chronic stress and anxiety, in which we all find ourselves to varying degrees, can reach a saturation point, leading to serious mental and physical health problems. Dependency on anxiety and stress can act like addiction changing the brain and its signals by constant negative imprints.

While stress will never be completely eliminated from our lives, it can be controlled. That control begins with knowledge. Understanding the truth about what occurs in the brain and body when the stress cycle remains unchecked is the first step in empowering us to break the debilitating cycles of worry, alarm and anxiety.

Degrees of anxiety can now be measured with brain imaging. Combinations of proteins with their DNA exert control over behavior. Proteins, often described as genes, do not cause the symptoms of mental illness, they change the circuits of the brain. Prolonged stress and anxiety, continual addictive behaviors, or chronic post-traumatic stress disorder actually change in time the DNA make-up of the brain cells that promote control over the limbic/basal ganglia relationship. With these changes come increased rates of depression and attempted suicide.

In the future, psychiatrists will be able to routinely use brain imagery to track changes or swab the inside of the mouth to measure the presence of certain types of gene action and response. Some individuals have gene structures more prone to serious management of stress, whereas others manage stress from multiple parts of the brain.

Genetic factors control the function of serotonin, the neurotransmitter of the frontal/prefrontal cortex. Some gene patterns are more prone to anxiety and, hence, lack the support systems in the brain to compensate. They have fewer serotonin pumps, so they have less serotonin coursing through the brain to activate the executive functions of the prefrontal lobe.

Genes have been identified that are the keys to the degree of anxiety being experienced. Moderate anxiety routes the brain's impulses from the amygdala to the prefrontal cortex where the executive function determines the causes and resultant anxiety. With severe anxiety, stress, and fear, the amygdala stimulates the limbic part of the brain and in turn the basal ganglia to deal with its primitive "fight or flight" strategies.

The Survival Mode of "Fight or Flight"

Sometimes, temporary effects of anxiety and stress are a necessity for our protection and well-being. But if prolonged into indefinite periods of time, there can be deleterious and even permanent adverse effects on brain and body.

A real or perceived threat can activate a rapid series of connections in the brain allowing the person to deal with protective emergencies which require "fight or flight." This physiological response is initiated by the basilar portion of the brain defined earlier in this text as the basal ganglia. To review, the functions of the basal ganglia are designed to protect the individual through four basic drives—self-preservation, bodily appetite, fear of death and sensuality. When specifically activated in one of these four functions, the basal ganglia send a message to the limbic system in the central part of the brain—the part of the brain that initially processes emotions.

The emotion message is then sent to the prefrontal area of the brain for value judgment and decision making. In a state of alarm the brain transmission is immediate, as the basal ganglia and limbic system have done their jobs putting into place a sophisticated and complex emergency response system. Until the emergency problem is resolved, the prefrontal cortex remains in an anxiety state to direct protected and safety processes.

Stuck in a State of Alert

If the stress factor is provoked too often or prolonged for long periods of time the brain becomes less adaptive. An individual under chronic stress, with no hope of relief from fear or from recurrent negative indulgence, can be constantly on guard and never able to relax. This high state of alert is particularly egregious in children and young adults. The prefrontal cortex cannot deal with the constant anxiety and begins to slow and shut down.

In a previous chapter, we described the affect of stress on the brain as a computer whose circuitry has been compromised in an endless loop. While the executive portion of the brain is shutting down, the activity of the basal ganglia and limbic systems persist in their activity and cannot shut off. The computer freezes and the response becomes a sensation of continual unpleasant anxiety. The feeling of being stuck is a literal physiological phenomenon and the result is ultimately depression.

The Fight for Agency

As the depression/anxiety cycle persists (also seen in addictive behaviors), an indefinite number of nerve cells are lost. Like the cartoon zebra, we begin to lose our "stripes." The basal ganglia and limbic system no longer serve the prefrontal cortex, but take over control of the brain. Decision making and freedom of choice are impaired and eventually lost. This process is particularly true with addictive disorders, as the brain in a state of chronic discomfort and apprehension, "demands" a repetition of the exciting experience.

The Chemical Response

The chemical responses to stress are detailed in the accompanying illustrations. Upon exposure to stress, the nerve cells of the basal ganglia (Figure 6) secrete an enzyme called corticotropin-releasing factor (CRF). The pituitary gland under the basal ganglia is the master gland of all other hormone-producing glands in the body. Stimulated by the corticotropin-releasing factor, the pituitary gland releases adrenocorticotropic hormone (ACTH), which passes through the bloodstream to the adrenal gland located on top of the kidneys. The adrenal gland then excretes steroids called glucocorticoids. Glucocorticoids have a marked effect on metabolism, weight gain, weight loss, immune function, heart rate and the behavioral response to stress.

Figure 7 shows the continued flow of corticotropin-releasing factor (CRF) in mental illness associated with chronic stress and

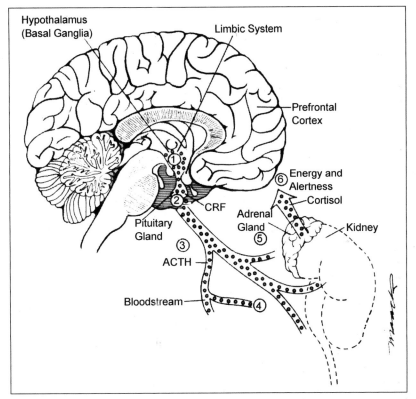

Figure 6. The hypothalamic-pituitary-adrenal (HPA) axis allows you to respond quickly when you're faced with a threat. However, in some people with anxiety disorders, this system remains in overdrive.

anxiety. The brain/body relationship is kept in an ongoing state of alert. Long-term effects on the brain demonstrated by neuroimagery from functional MRI scans show the significant slowing of frontal and prefrontal lobe function. More serious effects include the loss of brain tissue. Such changes are the basis of many forms of mental

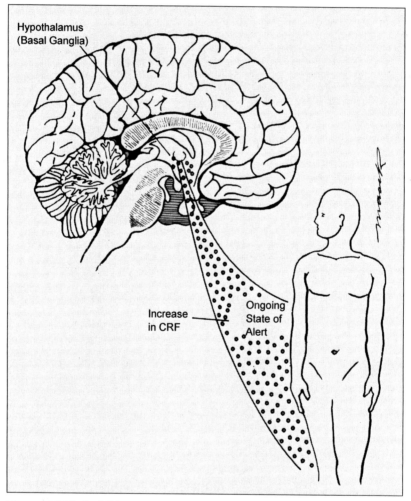

Figure 7. With the HPA axis in overdrive, the body is in an ongoing state of alert. Brain and bodily systems suffer. The basilar brain demands temporary relief by indulgence in the addictive habit which perpetuates the addiction. The cycle goes on.

disturbance and mental illness, and help us to more clearly define abnormalities of sexual behavior, drugs, violence and addictive disorders for all ages.

These physiological descriptions beg the question—can these serious changes be stopped, reversed, and regenerated? Can the zebra regain his stripes?

Yes. The critical DNA can change back to a normal relationship within the prefrontal cortex.

Chapter 9

The Risks of Our Changing Times

"Wilt thou be made whole?"

—John 5:6

Exercise (or lack thereof)

Time was when a new bike was a favorite and much-hoped-for Christmas or birthday gift. Today's teens like things in small packages like iPods and cell phones and other gizmos and gadgets proffered by the electronic world.

Time was when an adolescent would walk to the store or the park or the swimming hole. Today's teens want the keys to the car—or a car of their own.

Time was when everyone sat down for dinner prepared by mom with food groups and nutrition in mind. Today's teens eat more and more meals at the drive-thru, hang out at the mall, watch television or sit at the computer. Some just "chill."

What they don't do is exercise.

Even worse are those with addictions including depression, anxiety, substance abuse, gambling, pornography, weight loss and eating disorders. They have slumped into a pattern of regressive behavior with "a brain gone wrong."

Exercise is a primary means of keeping the brain growing and developing in teenage years. No question, nerves in the brain can be changed in favor of positive or negative imprinting. Exercise plays a part in the process.

Exercise increases the blood supply to all organs including the brain. Nerve cells are enhanced in the process. Exercise also affects the relationship between mind, body and spirit. Mental health research shows that vigorous exercise not only boosts that relationship and makes it whole but also preventively makes it better.

So why is Jared staring blankly at a screen—television, cell, computer—when he could be building such connectors?

Modern neurology has found that one of the major centers of learning and memory in the left temporal lobe of the brain, the hippocampus, is affected by exercise. Just a few months of active exercise increases both the size and function of this part of the brain. This same effect can be measured in the prefrontal cortex. Imaging of the brain of a healthy child or youth will show rapid growth and activity while that of an adult will show a lesser degree or increase. But everyone's brain prospers with exercise.

Three areas of growth within the brain are intensified by exercise. Most important is the prefrontal cortex (the uniquely human part of the brain), the hippocampus in the left temporal lobe of the brain, and the perceptual pathways that transfer information from one part of the brain to the other.

For many years medical science has known that vigorous exercise can release chemicals called endorphins that rush a "high" through the body. Some youth call the release of endorphins a feel-good sensation. Endorphins help treat depression, short or long bouts with the disease. Recently, brain scientists have identified chemicals that bring about permanent changes in the brain which help teens overcome and rebound from mental illness. These chemicals, similar to immune substances or hormones, carry messages from the brain to other organs of the body. These organs reciprocate with messages to the brain. The protein IGF-1 and the chemical called BDNF combine to direct the brain to form new cells and the interconnections with other brain dendrites.

How is it done? Exercise stimulates new nerve growth in the prefrontal cortex of the brain. Vigorous exercise of muscles launches a number of these transmissions. What happens is opposite to "a brain gone wrong." Specific chemicals that connect mind and body enhance morals, values and spiritual development by updating the prefrontal cortex with new dendrites.

Any program that promotes exercise—Family Home Evening, individual and competitive sports or outdoor recreation—should be initiated when children are in their early youth. Physical exercise can then become a way of life, especially if youth see their parents involved in exercise or sports. A game of volleyball in the back yard or sledding as a family, a pick-up basketball or soccer game with other youth in the neighborhood—these are hearty and fun ways to get exercise.

Competitive sports organizations sponsored by neighborhoods, schools, communities and church groups are fulfilling and provide both practices and organized games or matches. These team or individual sports require more than competition, they thrive on practice. Exercise. An added bonus is when parental support or coaching is involved and team work and sportsmanship can be taught.

Those who prefer less organized activity can find dancing, running, Pilates, judo or aerobics a great release. Yardwork, helping clean up a local eye-sore, service projects for neighbors and friends or working at the grocery carrying bags for customers are also good activities to stretch muscles as as well as the brain.

For children and youth, time away from the addictive habits of TV, computers, hard rock music and electronic games, negates artificial stimulus experienced by the "couch potato." Studies show an actual decrease in new development of brain cells among children and teens that spend hours mesmerized by visual and auditory stimuli. Often this absorption leads to other addictive behaviors as the stimulus is lowered to a much baser level and again, DNA is at risk of being reprogrammed or permanently degraded.

High energy drinks

Time was when water out of the hose was a welcome refreshment for the neighborhood baseball game and bottled water sounded like something your mother canned on the kitchen stove. Today, teens haul high energy drinks in their backpacks and in the name of "keeping going" they chug them down like water.

Energy drinks with high caffeine content registered sales last year in the U.S. of three billion dollars. The question is, "What is the expense to both mind and body of indulging in these escalating compounds?"

Just when you thought you found a way to keep the kids hydrated and happy, you learn the actual implications of high energy drinks. Energy drinks go beyond the caffeine buzzes of soda pop. The acceleration of caffeine addiction is apparent in teens. Caffeine has addictive characteristics, even in smaller doses, and those with higher doses have resultant patterns within the brain that parallel other seemingly serious habit-forming drugs. The addiction rate appears to be proportionate to the quantity of caffeine indulged.

Again, the risk of "a brain gone wrong."

About 500 brands of high energy drinks reached U.S. shelves this past year. At the same time, the amount of use doubled. Eight million adolescents report that they regularly consume high caffeine content energy drinks. Among college students the consumption is reaching binge proportions.

A dangerous trend in college-age students is the combining of high energy drinks with alcohol or other drugs. The mix is said to decrease the feeling of intoxication, while propelling the user to a "high" from the limbic and basal ganglia areas of the brain. The brain actually experiences a higher incidence of psychotic delusions from high doses of caffeine. The heart races to the point of failure. The hormone system becomes skewed to the point of being dysfunctional. Permanent stress patterns override the prefrontal cortex and the basal ganglia takes over. The effect of caffeine is identified with the same effect that stress has on the body and brain.

Teens are beginning to model the practice seen in college-age students.

The hormonal effects on indulgent teens can interfere with physical growth and the development of adrenal, thyroid and sexual glands. Permanent high blood pressure and heart problems are on the increase because of foreign stimulants. In many parts of the country, 12 percent of those coming to emergency wards for treatment are afflicted with mind/body complications resulting from high caffeine indulgence and 12 percent of those require hospitalization for varying complications, some of which are fatal. Twenty-nine percent of those seen in emergency facilities combine use of caffeine with products that include various illicit drugs.

Although the Food and Drug Administration pressed for legislation to regulate high concentration of caffeine drinks in a drug controlled program, adolescents should be conscious of the risks.

It's cough syrup!!

Time was when a suffering child or teen would grimace at the thought of taking cough syrup. Today, adolescents are lapping it up as an antidote to whatever ails them and their brains are paying for the addiction.

Dextromethorphan is increasingly popular among teens because it is legally and easily available. These drugs are over the counter as cough and cold remedies. They are comparatively inexpensive and do not have the stigma associated with illegal substances.

The use of these drugs has skyrocketed ten times in the last three years. This increase reflects all ages, however, among adolescents, the number is 15 times that of the previous population three years ago.

The National Institute of Mental Health and the Federal Drug Administration report that 75 percent of those experiencing addiction are adolescents. The figure peaks at ages 15 to 16 with 46 percent of those treated for drug use considered the "abuse class" and 42 percent in the "addictive" category. Both groups have benefited from treatment in psychotherapy, as well as group sharing. Individual therapy, however, is the most important. Those with dependency issues need daily outpatient care or inpatient residential treatment in the cases of more serious problems.

Adolescents admitted to residential treatment centers usually require psychotherapeutic medication. Some require methadone, baprenorphine, or naltrexone, all three of which are utilized in adult centers. Increasing numbers of youth are admitted to hospitals with life-threatening respiratory depression requiring intubations and heart/lung machine intervention to maintain life.

Medical problems resulting from cough syrup abuse include marked sedation, inability to think and concentrate and gastrointestinal problems (including vomiting and diarrhea), rapid heart beat and heart failure. The effects on the brain are typical of other addictions, with the basal ganglia and limbic systems taking over.

If the extent of abuse is not known, medical examinations should include inquiry into possible dextromethorphan (the active ingredient in cough syrup) usage. Parent awareness and discussion with teens is the first and most influential line of defense.

The beat goes on.

Time was when the works of Ludwig von Beethoven were revered as the finest music in the world. He was known to compose entire symphonies in his head, hearing the part of every instrument before he put a single note on paper. He claimed, "Music is a higher revelation than all wisdom and philosophy. Music is the electrical soil in which the spirit lives, thinks and invents."

Today's music is indeed "electric" but of another kind and far less engaging or sustaining. In essence, it induces evil by its diabolical invitation to the brain to compromise its possibilities.

Music is wonderful when it evokes a positive response form the limbic system on through the right hemisphere of the brain and then to the higher centers in the frontal and prefrontal lobe of the brain. And you thought you were just listening! Music has its roots and its expression in the brain. The emotional feelings can be uplifting, reaching spiritual even ecstatic dimensions. Music in its many forms, either instrumental or choral, can be enjoyed as an individual experience or as a cohesive moment for a group, such as in a religious setting, concert or performance. Music relieves stress and tension and elevates the spirit.

Some, even most, modern teenage music, however, is characteristically loud, hostile and sensual. The notes, if there are any, do not activate the brain with pleasure and higher-level functions, but instead remain a function of the basal ganglia. This music, often loud and lacking in any form of melody, stimulates all of the more primitive responses like anxiety, flight, fear, hostility, and anger. In addition, the selfish and sensual parts of the basal ganglia are engaged.

The three-per-second heavy beat of rock music is identical in rate to the cybernating electrical activity within the basal ganglia of the brain. The result is mutual stimulation between the rhythm of the music and the rhythm of the basal ganglia.

These modern rhythms are highly addictive as are the antisocial and sensual language of the songs. They make a place for other addictions of a perverse sexual nature and often introduce harmful and addictive drugs. Many teenagers not only listen, they wear earphones so as not to miss a beat.

Day after day the music blasts in their rooms, their cars and their heads. Unless their music is played, they become tense and uncomfortable. Both are signs of addiction. Unlike classical or wholesome music, the three-second beat rhythms wedge into the life and pattern of a teen as an addiction.

A recent study in Great Britain—home of many a rock band—determined that these rhythms have been found to interfere with or retard certain types of physical or chemical reactions in non-living molecules. And this is what our teens are taking into their heads!

Not all current music is so extreme, although most music videos add a near-pornographic dimension to the incessant beat.

Music can lift and encourage. It can leave a youth whistling and humming a tune. It can match Beethoven's "electrical soil in which the spirit lives, thinks and invents." But such activity requires a high-functioning brain.

Video games

Time was when parents held the line. After school, work on the farm or in local businesses was expected in most homes to help make ends meet. When Sally wanted a new sweater, she worked for it. Today's parents are afraid to set limits. "If I don't give in now, if I make these rules, little Jared or Sally will rebel later on."

Conversely, setting no limits will assure that Jared and Sally will struggle later on.

Many of the problems with teens today can be traced to violent video games, television programs and movies. Students act out the scenes on their screens because reality has become what they take in day after day. That reality is violence.

Teens that play violent video games show definite changes in MRI brain scans. Using functional Magnetic Resonance Imagery, adolescents who were playing video games showed loss of prefrontal lobe function. The amygdala stimulated the basal ganglia to take control as the imprinting of brain cells called for increased anger, tension, and trauma.

Oddly enough, the trauma is just beginning, because the loss of brain power will be manifest in more than MRI scans. A teenager addicted to violent video games or other violent media risks a greater likelihood of violent behavior and further addictions beyond just screen play.

Why? Because the ability to reason, think, judge, and calculate has been diminished. They are not developing self-discipline; they are not learning to be charitable to others; they are not studying, playing outside, or talking to anyone. Even their cell phones and instant messages may take a secondary position when the video games are in control.

Parents complain about the hours wasted playing video games. But time is not all that is wasted. Brain scan comparisons of those who obsess with video games and those who don't, show graphically that the group of non-playing teens exhibited more activation in the frontal cortex. In other words, the dendrites were multiplying and the brain was functioning at a higher level. The group fixated with violence showed diminished function in the prefrontal cortex and increased activity in the right amygdala, as well as activation in the right basal ganglia more than the left. In other words, they had slipped into more animal-like instincts.

What can be done?

Decide in advance what time limits will be placed on video game activity. This would be an effective discussion for Family Home Evening which will hopefully bring a consensus. But if you have to make a parental decision, don't give in. Don't risk compromising the brain and its burgeoning power.

1. The argument "everyone is doing it" is not new. Only the medium is different. The response of decades ago still holds today. Hold the line as parents.

2. The argument, "You don't love me" is an indication that love is being measured in things not relationships. Work at spending time together, reading, finding new interests, sitting on the lawn and having a chat.

3. The argument, "I'm the only one who doesn't have . . ." is youthful perception not reality. Reinforce what they do have, which is parents who love them and a family who enjoys and needs their company.

4. The argument, "I'm bored" is an invitation to join a swim club, get a bird feeder, build a club house or any other project that will stimulate thinking and doing.

5. The argument, "I hate to read. . ." is an opportunity to read as a family. Scripture study is reading with a purpose and a promise of the presence of the Spirit. Get each child a library card. Make regular trips to the library to seek out the great literature of Twain, Dickens and others. Biographies of great leaders

whose childhood and youth was not marred by "a brain gone wrong" may also be instructional as well as entertaining. Children who play video games have reduced reading comprehension of books of 200 pages or more when compared with those who read often.

There may well be other arguments for which you will find answers and even solutions. If you have set pre-determined goals with your children and set expectations as a family, you will emerge stronger. Others may be persuaded to follow your lead if you and your adolescent children are seen as happy and at ease with yourselves and each other. And there may be fewer battles in the future.

Eating disorders

Time was when stick figures were just what you drew on the board to represent people. The desirable shape for women was curves and more curves. Today, stick figures speak thin. "You can never be too thin" is broadcast in advertisements and films. "Thin is in" and weight is nothing more than flab. Get rid of it, society shouts.

Youth believe it. Not only do they avoid food from all the appropriate groups that promise health and fitness, they find ways to push food from their diet and the brain begins to starve. Again, the brain goes wrong.

Youth in many modern cultures have more choices and opportunities than ever before. This is especially true of young women. With opportunity comes the moral balance of a God-given responsibility to use their agency wisely.

Counter to the blessing of freedom, our society is experiencing an accelerated rate of eating disorders, the large majority of which are adolescents and young women. Fads, social undercurrents, ego conflicts and personal struggles have brought on dangerous eating disorders.

The motivation to be thin continues to rise. With adolescents, thin has become synonymous with attractiveness. In addition, the media has incessantly flashed the message, "You must be thin and beautiful in order to be happy." Or, "You can never be too thin!" Fashion, too, is fixated on the slender, lithe body which very few can conjure up, even those with eating disorders. While most suffering from eating disorders are female, there are males who struggle as well.

There are three types of eating disorders. First is anorexia. Those with anorexia are fixated on weight loss independent of their body shape. Limitations of eating become progressively abnormal, with an intense fear of weight gain or being fat. Those addicted to this behavior deny the weight loss and its serious health consequences even though they are overly thin.

The second type is bulimia. This illness results in repeated intake of large amounts of food, followed by forced vomiting or excessive use of laxatives.

Both of these eating disorders, anorexia and bulimia, lead to the use of diet pills, diuretics (water pills), fiber supplements, excessive exercise or fasting. What is unfortunate is that the bulimic's image of "thin" is rarely reached though the body is stripped of all its weight and strength.

The third condition is binge eating or compulsive over-eating. With this abnormal pattern, food intake is uncontrolled and impulsive beyond the point of feeling full. Eating becomes a temporary source of overcoming anxiety or other forms of mental illness, such as depression or loneliness. Those with this illness become ashamed of overeating and anxiety escalates. The overeating process becomes addictive and out of control.

All three forms of eating disorders develop into serious addictive problems. Teens who feel an obsession to lose or gain weight, and who experience the resultant compulsion, give away their agency. That decision puts the prefrontal lobe in a precarious position.

The consequences of eating disorders are always serious. As the problem progresses it can escalate to a crisis or even fatality. Of all mental illnesses, those involved with eating disorders have the highest mortality rate.

Chemical imbalance in the brain follows the same abnormal neural transmitter characteristics as with other addictive disorders. The brain goes wrong, leading to an imbalance in all bodily systems including hormones. Loss of nutrients to organs leads to organ failure. Lack of blood sugar, proteins and essential chemicals results in multiple system shut-down. Decreased function of the organs leads to permanent damage and even death.

Eating disorders also generate mental illnesses which intensify ideas of self-harm and loss of mental control. Drug addictions may add to the downward spiral.

How are these disorders treated?

Both the bodily and mental problems of eating disorders can be life threatening. Residential or inpatient hospital treatment centers are the most effective. Psychiatric evaluation and a full medical evaluation are important. The most successful treatment relies upon the multi-disciplinary staff of professionals.

Outpatient care is often complicated by the highly deceptive and in-denial defenses that are common among patients with eating disorders. That problem, when present, is best handled in an inpatient facility or residential treatment center. The treatment team should involve an internist, psychiatrist, psychologist, social worker, specialty nurses and dieticians.

Return to educational, social, recreational and religious organizations are all vital. Family therapy is also essential and long-term care must be expected at all levels of treatment. Clearly, those with eating disorders are feeding "a brain gone wrong."

Section Two Introduction

A Brain Gone Wrong—on Its Own

"Let not your heart be troubled."

—John 14:27

NOT ALL MENTAL HEALTH CHALLENGES FACING OUR YOUTH are self-induced. Individuals differ in the challenges that create the greatest risk of developing a mental illness. If biological problems are very high, the person can become ill even when they have strong, loving families, positive social support, and good coping skills. Another person may not have as many biological problems, but may become "pushed over the edge" by excess stress, trauma, or because they have few resources for coping with their challenges.

Why do children and youth fail to achieve normal psychological and social development? Why do they falter in academic learning or balanced productivity? Why do they lose touch with family or suddenly shift their social circles? These questions haunt our society. In the last decade, advances in behavioral science have begun to shape treatment and care that give hope to those who struggle.

Families facing these quandaries look in every direction for help. They turn to friends, religious leaders, school personnel and the family doctor. Some even try to diagnose by using the Internet.

The complexities of life and the way we address them demand that parents, families and mental health professionals work together. The need for such interventions was never more acute. Past therapies have failed to integrate and correlate all levels of research diagnosis, therapeutic planning, implementation and follow-up. Critical to success is the involvement of the family as part of the process. The most effective approach is to draw upon mental health professionals who circle the child and family with experts in a handful of disciplines.

Chapter 10

The Bipolar Dilemma

"And the peace of God, which passeth all understanding,
shall keep your hearts and minds through Christ Jesus."

—*Philip. 4:7*

Bipolar disorder strikes youth and even children and stays with them for a lifetime. The National Institute of Mental Health has found that bipolar disorders occur in two to three percent of the total population—one percent of children and youth.

Mood swings which characterize the illness occur wildly from manic phases to depression. Those in a manic state are characterized by ecstatic and grandiose ideas; the same day or several days later they may slip into depression and unhappiness. These rapid fluctuations of mood and behavior in all ages are common signs of bipolar disorder but are particularly exaggerated in childhood. Most cases tend to share similar symptoms at times with other mental health disorders.

The characteristics of bipolar disease often resemble the syndromes of attention-deficit disorder or the less common pattern of mental illness called Tourette Syndrome. Bipolar disorder, attention deficit disorder and Tourette Syndrome have been classified by behavioral scientists as a distinct triad of three illnesses associated with an abnormality between emotional make-up and executive functions of the brain in the prefrontal cortex. Previous chapters have addressed damage inflicted on this portion of the brain by addictions.

None of these three disorders is brought on by conscious action. Instead, each is associated with abnormalities of the more basal functions of the brain, called basal ganglia, which, once again, are the areas of self-preservation, bodily appetite, fear of death and sensuality. The disturbance between the emotions—both the primitive and the more highly developed—and the function of the prefrontal cortex are abnormalities of the so-called executive syndromes. The result is an inability of the victim to achieve appropriate and normal behavior patterns or expressions of executive decisions of the brain. The prefrontal cortex of these three syndromes is less active than normal and at times an abnormal brain imagery or indication of a lack of nerve tissue are present in the frontal and prefrontal cortex of those diagnosed with these syndromes.

The abnormality of the limbic portion of the nervous system is displayed by the brain's inability to appropriately send emotion signals, particularly to the prefrontal cortex. The same is true of the basal ganglia, which with its abnormal functioning can produce surges or emotional expression that are more than normal feelings or responses.

What are manic episodes?

Looking back on personal emotional feelings, most of us recall times of great happiness or joy, even ecstasy or euphoria. These feelings of supreme well-being can be manifest in adolescence and carry on into adulthood. These are normal sensations that we all have, particularly as we reflect on the past. We all wish we could recapture that energy and emotional intensity.

Such expressions of emotional feeling and behavior are different with bipolar disorder. In those cases of mental illness, the energy is cranked up to an excessive, sometimes excruciatingly high level. This overly high manic state is the defining characteristic of bipolar disorder.

Manic patients demonstrate excess excitation, abnormal talkativeness, sometimes amusing and frequent hyperactivity. At times those with the syndrome are grossly disorganized even to the point of losing contact with reality, which medical professionals call psychotic behavior. The problems are so extreme that at other times they may require physical restraints or even require injectable medications to lower the sensation to a more normal emotion and behavior. Severe irritability is a common indication of bipolar disorder, particularly in youth. Usually more than a short-lived episode, it can evolve into extreme anger.

Manic children and adolescents or even adults can place themselves and others in danger. Alcohol, tobacco and drugs magnify the problem.

What is the treatment?

The treatments of bipolar disorder are at times similar to major depression, including the use of the same medications. Important differentiation from other disorders is the prescribed medication. Medicines used for depression, such as serotonin reuptake inhibitors, can actually cause severe side effects in cases of bipolar disorder.

The medications for treatment of bipolarity are extremely valuable, taken alone. However, they cannot address the wide range of psychological, social and behavioral issues related to the disorder. This is why psychotherapy has a central role in a comprehensive treatment plan.

Psychotherapy can maximize the effectiveness of drug therapy, especially when it is in combination with education about the illness and also with necessary support services, ranging from family to supportive friendships. Among other benefits, psychotherapy can help youth with bipolar disorder reduce stress, rebuild relationships and reinforce self-worth.

Medications used in the treatment of bipolar disorder

Lithium has been prescribed for several decades in the treatment of bipolar disorder. This and other similar medications do have side effects at times and, therefore, are generally avoided in treating children.

Mood stabilizers such as Tegretol, Depakote and Lamictal are the main prescribed drugs. These stabilize the relationship between the left and right hemispheres of the brain and help control the abnormal input of emotional charges from the limbic as well as the basal ganglia areas of the brain.

In combination with mood stabilizers, atypical antipsychotics are used. These substances reduce the anxiety and extreme stress associated with bipolarity. These substances are used in early small dosages as compared with their usage in other conditions, such as psychotic or schizophrenic disorders. The degree of dosage is approximately 1/5 to 1/10 of those used in the above mentioned serious illnesses. The compounds are called Risperdal, Seroquel, Zyprexa, Geodon and Abilify.

These medications do more than stop the symptoms of irrational and wide mood swings that are sometimes associated with hallucinations and delusions incident to the disorder. They are particularly valuable as an adjunct to the mood stabilizers and they appear to work in a complimentary fashion to reduce the over-activity of the limbic system and the basal ganglia. This allows for an increase in serotonin in the frontal cortex and the gradual reduction of dopamine and acetylcholine in the limbic system and also the basal ganglia. Such a change with increase in serotonin allows for the development of normal frontal lobe functioning, particularly in the uniquely human endowment of the prefrontal cortex.

The medication management may be prolonged for a period of several months or years. After a period of no symptoms for six or twelve months it may be stopped. Monitoring during this subsequent follow-up period is essential with professionals that are psychotherapists, therapists, or physicians (psychiatrists) trained to treat bipolar disorders.

Chapter 11

Attention-Deficit Hyperactivity Disorder

"The race is not to the swift, nor the battle to the strong."

—Eccl. 9:11

ATTENTION-DEFICIT HYPERACTIVITY DISORDER was first described in 1845 by Dr. Heinrich Hoffman, a sometime poet who also wrote books on medicine and psychiatry. Dr. Hoffman penned a story complete with illustrations for his three-year-old son titled, "The Story of Fidgety Philip." The tale was a perfect description of a little boy who had Attention-Deficit Hyperactivity Disorder (ADHD).

Since that time, millions of children have struggled with the symptoms of inattention, impulsiveness, hyperactivity, restlessness and day-dreaming. Despite persistent skepticism, this most common childhood psychiatric disorder is increasingly understood to be a brain malfunction. Because of modern therapeutic techniques, young people with ADHD can look forward to a bright outlook of total recovery.

Today, the use of educational techniques in the school environment, extra school educational programs, and (of more recent interest) the use of biofeedback, or neurofeedback are making a difference. Biofeedback has been used by specialists for decades, but the new instrumentation and methodology of measuring brain waves has made this a very significant functional treatment, which perhaps could be a dominant approach for ADHD in the future.

In addition, enhanced versions of older drugs are being introduced and new ones are being offered for treatment. Methods of therapy beyond use of medications are gaining increased interest, power and effectiveness and the many "fidgety Philips" are settling down.

Different forms of the disorder may have different biological roots. Discoveries in neuroscience are re-informing the growing consensus that ADHD is not just a set of behavioral problems, but a biologically based disorder of brain function. The symptoms of impulsiveness, inattentiveness, distractibility and hyperactivity arise, the research suggests, because of misfiring of the brain's executive function in the prefrontal cortex making it difficult to stay still, concentrate and exercise forethought and self-control.

ADHD is specifically an inability to relate information between the hemispheres of the brain in the learning process, as well as an inability to transmit that information as it is developed by the left and right hemispheres of the brain up to the prefrontal cortex for value judgment and ultimate decision making. In addition, information from the prefrontal cortex down to the limbic system and the basal ganglia of the brain is found to be defective and slow in people with ADHD. The cause of this abnormality is a deficiency of formation and transmission capabilities in both directions through the system of nerve pathways.

The brain's inability to produce a specific enzyme, as well as adequate amounts of norepinephrine, has been most incriminated in recent research. Norepinephrine is critical for normal transmission within perceptual pathways of the brain.

ADHD is known to have a strong genetic component—one of the highest in psychiatric disorders. Similar symptoms have also been identified in the so-called executive syndromes, which include (in addition to ADHD) bipolar disorder and Tourette Syndrome. Research has also discovered that abnormal hormonal make-up of the uterus and the placenta during pregnancy can contribute to the development of ADHD or the increase toward genetic predisposition.

Distortions come from the reversal of two hormones called cate-cholamines and prostaglandins. Proper ration of these two hormones from the uterus and placenta are essential for the optimal formation of the embryonic and fetal brain. Anxiety, tension, anger, and distress, particularly among adolescents who are pregnant, may give rise to this distortion. Though the child may be adopted after birth, it is sobering to note that 45 percent of children with ADHD treated in child psychiatric practices were born out of wedlock to a young and disturbed mother. This certainly points to the additional gravity and consequences of unwed teenage mothers. While society is trying desperately to support such young women, the case can be made that the focus should be on not getting pregnant and not having sex out of marriage, if we hope to stem this growing affliction.

Those with ADHD benefit from medications generally entitled "psychomotor stimulants." According to the national survey on children's health in this country, as well as in most European nations, children and adolescents ages 4 to 17 with ADHD measure about 5.5 percent of the population. Approximately 50 percent of those with the diagnosis are taking stimulant medications.

The most important recent development in the drug treatment of ADHD is the increased use of new formulations of these stimulants. There are now nearly two dozen versions of methylphenidate and dextroamphetamine under the old brand names of Ritalin and Dexedrine and the more recent labels, Concerta, Metadate, Focalin, Methylin, Adderall, and Dextrostat. Added labels like LA (long acting) and XR or ER (extended release) refer to a gradual or staged release of the drug into the blood stream, rather than an immediate one.

Both children and parents prefer the long-acting and extended-release forms, which last eight to twelve hours instead of four to six. Children experience fewer ups and downs with the long-acting medications. They do not suffer the inconvenience of taking the drug three or four times a day, or the embarrassment of taking it at school. Recent studies show that they are less likely to cease the regimen than those taking short-acting formulas. The most widely used brand to-day is Concerta, a type of extended release methylphenidate with effects that last twelve hours.

Concern has grown about the risks of stimulant medication. Some discussion among professionals and families points to an increased incidence of problems with depression including thoughts of suicide or even suicidal attempts of those using psychomotor stimulation. Concerns are unfounded.

Studies by the National Institute of Mental Health also conclude that these highly used compounds do not have adverse psychiatric effects like prompt aggression, hostility or suicide. The Food and Drug Administration has explored the need to restrict these medications and the related information when dispensed pharmaceutically. It appears that those patients who have been referred to as having cardiovascular disease actually had preexistent heart problems.

Still, some are not convinced. During the last several decades, some spiritual groups and organizations have actually published their own material suggesting the medications have serious harmful effects. They have also attacked the use of serotonin reuptake inhibitors, such as Prozac, and claim such inhibitors prompt suicide. There is no such evidence.

Dextroamphetamine and methylphenidate are also addicting. They have been found to be addictive when used intravenously. When taken orally, these medications have been found to process too slowly for the brain to produce addiction. The hippie generation of the 1960s used them intravenously. Therefore, the FDA labeled these substances as "controlled" to prevent addiction.

Recent literature has also indicated that ADHD medications actually lower the risk of a predisposition to later addiction. Extensive studies show there is no indication that taking ADHD medications affects the rate of addiction in later life.

A new product, Strattera, has already been observed as benefiting children ten years of age or older and is definitely one of the primary choices for adolescents. Occasionally it produces a reduced sleep pattern in the first two days of usage, but this can adjust significantly during the medication regimen. It is not a psychomotor stimulant medication. Its slow release forms of methylphenidate and dextroamphetamine have become popular with adults who suffer from ADHD.

Learning disabilities and ADHD: What's the difference?

Professors from Harvard, George Washington University and North Carolina University have stated strongly that there is no difference between ADHD and learning disabilities. They are the same thing! Studies show that 90 percent of symptoms overlap between both syndromes. The problem of perceptual processing difficulties, either auditory or visual, is found equally in both sexes and is found in all cases that are truly diagnosed as ADHD in adults. There has been a tendency for educators and school personnel in the past to classify learning disabilities as a distinct condition, contrasted or compared with ADHD.

Who has ADHD?

ADHD is not necessarily something you grow out of. Tracking those with ADHD as children has shown that approximately one-third will carry symptoms into adulthood. Less than 10 percent of the adult population will face an onset of ADHD not tied to childhood.

The number of adults receiving treatment for ADHD has more than doubled in the last few years. Symptoms may interfere with daily life more in adults than in children because adults generally require more self-control, planning and calculated strategies.

In 2003 a national survey included ADHD in its questioning for the first time. Approximately 3 percent of adults ages 18 to 44 received the ADHD diagnosis, about half the rate found in children. The only childhood risk factor for persistence into adulthood was severity of symptoms.

ADHD is much more common in boys than girls, but adult women are now using ADHD drugs just as frequently as men the same age. Some think that symptoms are more easily recognized in boys whose behavior can be more troublesome and who are prone to acting out. Hence, ADHD in young girls may be masked by less hyperactivity. There is no difference between the challenges both sexes face who have learning disabilities.

Identifying ADHD in adults can be tricky. Like finding a missing jigsaw puzzle piece, ADHD in adults may identify more clearly the problems which have been mis-labeled as laziness, character flaws or learning disabilities. Medications, group social skills training, individual psychotherapy, vocational counseling and coaching may be helpful for adults with ADHD. The first controlled study of cognitive behavior therapy for adults with ADHD published last year found improvements in complications such as anxiety, depression and attention issues, validating the need for treatment through psychotherapy as well as medication management.

Those with ADHD, independent of their age, have either visual or auditory perceptual processing problems. Surprisingly, this phenomenon has characterized a number of famous people who have made legendary contributions to society. Take Albert Einstein. He had a marked visual perceptual processing problem that made him unable to read until he was nine years old. He was labeled for many years as slow and inconsistent; yet, he was brilliant. Winston Churchill had perception problems and was stumped by mathematics beyond simple addition or subtraction. Thomas Edison and John F. Kennedy had auditory perceptual problems; both experienced childhood and adolescent communication disorders. The son of President John F. Kennedy, John Jr., had just the opposite genetic characteristic—he suffered from visual perceptual problems. He failed the Bar exam three times in Massachusetts and New York and finally was able to complete the test when Harvard University recommended that he take the test auditorily. He passed with excellent marks.

What other forms of management might be considered?

Not all ADHD is the same. Three major researchers—Dr. Joseph Bideman, professor of child and adolescent psychiatry at Harvard University, Dr. Larry Silver, professor of psychiatry at George Washington University and Dr. Russell Barkley, professor of psychiatry at North Carolina University—have clarified that a dozen formats with nerve pathway differences all center on the single diagnosis of ADHD. These alternative patterns of the syndromes at times give rise to challenges with the use of medications now available. New therapy techniques may radically change the approach to the treatment of ADHD, particularly those variant forms which become a challenge to conventional medications.

Despite the absence of negative conclusions in the medical literature, many parents and even professionals remain skeptical about medication. Concerns about long-term effects, combined with the problem that many children and adolescents do not want to take medication, encourage a search for alternatives. Preliminary evidence shows that psychosocial treatment is significantly helpful as an adjunct to medication.

The modern approach to psychotherapy with those suffering from a form of ADHD is to correct and solve the problems of multiple symptoms. More than 50 percent of children have a combination of ADHD features—conduct disorder, depression, oppositional and defiant disorder and some behavioral disorder problems. Adults are not immune.

Childhood ADHD can extend into adulthood.

Children, particularly with ADHD, should not watch television for more than one hour a day. Exposure to hours of rapid imagery and scene changes—in television and video games—make non-virtual life boring by comparison and even slow or divert brain development. Cause and effect are not exactly clear, but what is clear is that our children receive too much of this form of visual stimulation. According to studies from the American Academy of Pediatrics and also the

Academy of Child and Adolescent Psychiatry, average exposure to television by age four is about three-and-a-half hours a day. These hours increase for many children as they mature into adolescence. Preoccupied or neglectful parents might let children watch too much television and children who love television may also become more susceptible (for genetic or social reasons) to hyperactivity and distraction.

Not far behind television is the "beat" that masquerades today as music. As with excessive stimulation from visual imagery, the modern extreme "rock rhythms" with their loud three-per-second beats can be damaging to the development of the nervous system as well.

Not only is less exposure to television and intense rock music good, but more exposure to nature—the sights, sounds and smells of the real world—is a much better activity for children, especially those with attention problems. Several recent studies have found that impulse control and other ADHD symptoms are countered by out-of-door activity and play close to nature. In spite of findings or scientific reasoning, more time outdoors in parks, playgrounds, woods, or fields boost a child's grasp of his environment and his part in the natural beauty of the world.

Biofeedback therapy is helping.

An alternative treatment is biofeedback therapy. This approach, which uses quantitative electroencephalography, takes advantage of modern electronic imagery instrumentality, creating a therapeutic approach called neurofeedback. Here's how it works. Magnet EEG (magneto electroencephalography—which has been defined quantitatively and with remarkably increased accuracy compared to older models) is capable of measuring as many as 300 spots on the surface of the scalp and the functioning of the nervous system beneath. This process pictures not only the cortex and surface of the brain, but the whole scope of the brain organ in terms of three-dimensional brain imagery. This has been a great asset in developing the improved biofeedback procedures.

What is biofeedback or neurofeedback?

1. EEG biofeedback, also known as neurotherapy, is a learning strategy that enables people to alter their own brainwaves.

2. When the information about a person's own brainwave characteristics is made available, he or she can learn to change them.

3. A person may want to change a particular behavior, but find it difficult or impossible to change despite working at it.

4. The Individual "plays" a type of computer game which exercises the brain, just as one can exercise the body while working out at the gym.

5. Through the non-invasive computer-accelerated exercise provided by the modern EEG neurotherapy, individuals are now capable of changing old behavior or adding new behavior which they felt unable to accomplish in the past.

6. The training is used for many conditions and disabilities in which the brain is not working as well as it might.

It is interesting to note that NASA (National Aeronautical Space Administration) utilized this new magneto form of computerized biofeedback when working with astronauts in preparation of their space flights. Clearly, the evolution of therapeutic techniques has come far. And we can be assured, it will continue to be advanced.

Chapter 12

The Ugliness of
Child Abuse and Neglect

*"Individuals who . . . abuse spouse or offspring . . . will
one day stand accountable before God."*

—*The Family: A Proclamation to the World*

Experiences in childhood profoundly influence the biological systems that govern responses to stress. Disturbances in a child's life—child abuse, neglect, and violence in what should be a safe environment—may exert a disproportionate influence creating the conditions ripe for childhood or adult depression, anxiety and post-traumatic stress symptoms.

You can see bumps and bruises. You can see the deflated smiles and the sunken eyes, the slumped shoulders, the cowering in the corner. Here's what you can't see—the body and brain adapting to acute distress such as a threat to survival or bodily integrity through the release of stress hormones. The hypothalamic-pituitary-adrenal axis (HPA) and the sympathetic nervous system respond with the development of these hormones to counter the stress. (See Figure 8.) To review, the hypothalamus at the base of the brain secretes corticotrophin-releasing factor (CRF) which stimulates the pituitary gland, and in turn gives rise to hormones that cause the excretion of cortisone and adrenaline compounds from the adrenal gland which sits on top of the kidneys. These hormones are necessary for the body to cope with challenges of "fight or flight." Blood pressure and blood sugar levels rise, breathing and heart rate increase, muscles tense and we feel anger, anxiety or fear. The system is controlled by feedback—a high level of stress hormone signals the hypothalamus to stop using CRF. If the stress, however, has been deep-seated or continues, then the hypothalamus continues to excrete the CRF hormone on almost a permanent basis.

This gives rise to major re-adjustments within the nervous system, which gradually diminish the function of the prefrontal cortex, the executive or decision-making portion of the brain. At the same time it will often intensify the formation of increased dopamine and the activity of the limbic system, which can create, and is the source of, either positive or negative emotions. The influence on additional hormones interferes with the learning process and we call this problem a perceptual deficit. Stressed children may see well and hear well, but they do not process well what they see and hear.

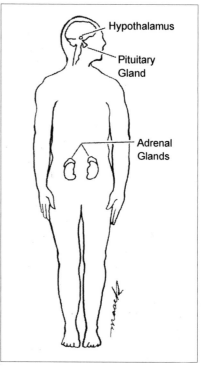

Figure 8. Intense emotions that go on chronically can evoke chemical changes in the glandular hormones of the body to activate adrenal hormones and influence the whole body.

If the stress response is provoked too often or for too long, it becomes less adaptive or flexible. A person under chronic stress, with no hope of relief is constantly on guard and never able to relax psychologically or physiologically. The feedback mechanism loses its sensitivity and the system fails to shut off.

Depression bears some resemblance to an acute stress response that persists when it is no longer needed. The hormonal mechanism previously described can be measured in children and youth with chronic stress syndromes. In these cases, it has been found that the CRF hormone is not only present in the blood stream, but is also abnormally high in the spinal fluid that bathes the brain.

Instead of being temporarily and appropriately alert and vigilant, a depressed person—child, youth, or adult—is likely to be chronically lethargic and apathetic or agitated, anxious and sleepless.

It has long been known that childhood abuse and neglect, as well as the loss of a parent, trigger adult psychiatric disorders. Depression, anxiety and post-traumatic symptoms are most common. Apart from hereditary and recent stress, childhood maltreatment is the most common predictor of major depression in adults. Researchers are now discovering how early experiences affect the ability to maintain psychological and physical balance. Childhood trauma and loss can cause prolonged hypersensitivity to stress by upsetting the regulation of the organs processing from the hypothalamus to the pituitary and to the adrenal cortex.

Receptors in the brain are sensitive to CRF in infancy and even before birth. A depressed mother raises the level of CRF in the child she is carrying. Six-month-old children of women who were depressed or abused while pregnant secrete cortisol at a higher than average level in response to mild stress. The mother, commonly an adolescent, can also have abnormalities in the hormones that are essential for growth and development of the fetus. These hormones are called catecholamines and prostaglandins. Some of the effects can be demonstrated experimentally by psychological testing as the child grows toward maturity.

We live in a day of abortions by the millions. Some are performed on teenagers who are pregnant out of wedlock. Emotional stress, anxiety, and anger radically distort the balance of hormones essential to the normal growth and development of the embryo and fetus. Those whose pregnancies reach full term face a life-changing decision. Do they keep the baby? Or do they place it for adoption? Some mental health problems such as ADHD and depression are consequences of the pregnancy of a teenager. Half the patients my colleagues and I have treated in the child/adolescent psychiatric facilities come from such pregnancies. Fortunately, the LDS Church Social Services program encourages a teen to have her baby adopted by an LDS family. The adopted children mature within that family environment. Their brains have the nerve cell plasticity to overcome the deficiencies created in the womb. If the child remains with the teenage mother, studies show the incidence of emotional adjustment problems is fully 100 percent.

Nonetheless, the increasing problem of teens with out-of-wedlock pregnancies is a major example of the need to follow the Lord's law of chastity before marriage.

Abortion among teenagers is a case study of its own. No one wins in the case of abortion. The mother who aborts carries the weight of that action all her life. It doesn't go away with a good marriage or after the delivery of a healthy child. It stalks the experience of raising a child and haunts the mother with what might have been. There is no rest from this sin except through the power of the Atonement of the Lord Jesus Christ.

People who suffer childhood maltreatment are more vulnerable to post-traumatic stress symptoms after further traumatic childhood or adult experiences because their bodies and brains have "learned" that they cannot count on protection and solace in distressing situations. The symptoms of post-traumatic stress disorder (PTSD) include heightened anxiety and jumpiness, intrusive memories and flashbacks, avoidance of situations, places and people reminiscent of the traumatic event, emotional numbness, loss of trust in others and an aversion to intimate relationships.

PTSD is usually preceded by an acute stress reaction that involves activity of the HPA axis and sympathetic nervous system. The amygdala, the brain center for registering fear and other emotions, intensifies memories of trauma through its links to the hypothalamus and other basal ganglia of the brain. It also relays information through the nervous system to the frontal lobe and particularly the prefrontal cortex, which is the seat of human moral and value decision making and executive decisions regarding behavior.

The aroused amygdala strengthens connections that produce emotionally charged memories. Its function is to make these memories difficult to eradicate so that we will recognize the threat if it reappears. In this way, traumatic experiences are preserved in long-term memory and everything even remotely reminiscent of the trauma may serve as a cue to revive the experience. Re-experiencing further strengthens the emotional associations while further consolidating the memory in a vicious cycle.

Excess cortisone production can damage the other basal ganglia of the brain, disrupting the connections between neurons and eventually causing the neurons themselves to degenerate. This degenerative process continues on up through the limbic system to the frontal cortex and even the prefrontal lobe. The resultant effect is the loss of ability for liberty of choice, executive decisions and agency. Pathological studies have shown actual reduction of brain tissue resulting from the chronic nature of post-traumatic stress disorder. Most disturbing of all, of course, is the loss of the prefrontal cortex, our uniquely human decision-making center of the brain.

Researchers are looking for ways to prevent and reverse the harm, either in childhood or late in life. We know that in adolescents there are approximately 20 percent of the total brain neurons that have not yet been formulated as neurological pathways of the brain. These can be integrated if the environment changes with the child or adolescent. The rehabilitation process is successful in utilizing the unused neurons of the nervous system. The antidepressant/antianxiety compounds called serotonin reuptake inhibitors are very helpful, particularly with adolescents and adults. These drugs actually assist in promoting the regeneration of neurons within the brain.

Drugs that interfere with anxiety of CRF are being developed also to aid in the treatment of depression and anxiety. Repetition of the frightening and anxious experiences of the past are minimized even after a matter of several weeks of treatment. The medication program combined with psychotherapy, particularly utilizing the cognitive behavioral therapy approach, is able to gradually prevent traumatic memories from working their way indelibly into the brain.

Psychological treatment for post-traumatic stress disorder then is a combined process of psychotherapy and medication. At times, however, particularly in young children who are not able to have serotonin reuptake inhibitors prescribed, psychotherapy is the only treatment. Fortunately, statistics show that this is just as effective in early childhood as treating with a combination of medication and psychotherapy in adolescents or young adults. Individual genetic characteristics modify the manifestations of the abnormal symptoms. Behavioral sciences have found genes that govern the reabsorption of serotonin, hence promoting greater activity in the amygdala.

Severe stress—parental loss, neglect, physical, sexual or emotional abuse—may also make a significant difference. But the greatest difference of all in the treatment process is the improvement or changing of the environment of the child to encourage the development of improved self-esteem, a sense of wellness and a resilience to stress in the future. As behavioral science has learned through brain imaging and molecular genetic studies, the science of healing will improve as we define more precisely the causes and nature of depression, anxiety and post-traumatic stress symptoms. Just as important, it may improve our understanding of how to specifically and more effectively deal with these tragic illnesses if treatment processes are not incorporated.

Circle the Wagons

"Behold, the Lord maketh the earth empty,
and maketh it waste, and turneth it upside down,
and scattereth abroad the inhabitants thereof."

—*Isaiah 24:1-6*

IN THIS BATTLE FOR THE MINDS AND SOULS of our precious youth, it seems fitting to call upon our rich heritage and summon up the same battle cry as was used by our Pioneer forefathers—"Circle the wagons!" The meaning then, as now, is to gather within a protected perimeter to defend what is most valuable to us. We can find strength in numbers as we muster every possible resource in defense of our youth and our families.

I've included a chapter on medical intervention in this resource section because I believe there are some wonderful medical therapies now available to help those suffering from disorders of the brain. It is encouraging to observe that many sincere mental health professionals—both within the Church and without—are implementing an interdisciplinary approach that is in the best interests of those struggling with addictions and other debilitating brain disorders. I have confidence that new medical and behavioral research will continue to come forth which will improve treatment for our struggling youth.

But I must emphasize that no therapy is complete without including the involvement of the family. Families guide the formation of society. In the future of society is dependent on the character imprinting of its individual members. Behavioral scientists have found that maturation of the brain reaches its fullest capacity in the environment of a family that is structured to correspond with the morals and values of the gospel of Jesus Christ. Within the circle of a loving family, the brain of a child and youth can be prepared and fortified to meet the challenges and evils of today's permissive society.

Chapter 13

Medical Intervention: Half the Solution

"O send out thy light and thy truth."

—Psalm 43:3

IF WE WERE ALL CARBON COPIES OF ONE ANOTHER, identifying the causes of mental illness and its proper treatment would be simpler; but unique differences in life experiences, temperament and biology make diagnosis and treatment a complex matter. No single treatment works for everyone; however, my experience points to a combination of medication and psychotherapy for optimal results. As a psychiatrist I have always been associated with an interdisciplinary team of mental health professionals, and have found the most success when frequent communication between the professionals is employed.

Who should be involved?

Mental health professionals need to collectively help each other understand what is going on in the life of the family and the child who comes for help. Interdisciplinary input at all levels of research, diagnosis and treatment produces the best results. The family must be a functional part of the involvement and decision-making process and be considered a focus of therapy along with the child or youth. Specifically, consideration should address the following four areas that shape personality and behavior.

- Biological
- Psychological

- Social structural
- Cultural (morals and values training based upon cultural choice)

A child with biologically based problems often has associated emotional and behavioral difficulties that require the integration of psychiatric, psychological, social work and educational involvement in both the planning and therapy process. Past therapies have often failed to integrate and correlate these processes, sometimes to the detriment of the therapeutic outcome.

One of the newest fields of behavioral science is biopsychiatry. Work in this field has produced dramatic changes in the diagnostic approach to behavior and mental illness. It has brought about specific medications for an array of hereditary and biologically based syndromes. These syndromes are often impeded by psychotherapy.

The process of research, diagnosis and treatment should be integrated between the various behavioral science disciplines of psychology, psychiatric social work and psychiatry. Diagnosis and treatment should have periodic and ongoing interdisciplinary involvement. Explanatory and intervention knowledge, as well as therapeutic strategies, should not be mutually exclusive. One blends into the other and therapy is best achieved when there is a continual cycling of all three.

This has not always been the case.

Behavioral scientists set up shop at the beginning of the 20th century. During my 55 years of post-graduate study and practice, I have seen the painful evolutionary struggle of our life sciences. I have seen so many in desperate need of answers. I am far from willing to accept the notion that we have arrived at a full truth. However, I am certain of the necessity of correlation with each of the branches of behavioral science as we move ahead. For me, that is an absolute. It stands as a caution to those who offer or accept a singular approach to treatment.

My dual specialties of child psychiatry and pediatrics began to flourish after World War I. A group of physicians and educators— Brenneman, Spitz, Gessel, Watson, Kanner—toured Europe in 1919 anxious to learn from the specialists who were pioneering behavioral science treatments. Up until then, earlier scientists including Kraeplin, Freud, and Pavlov had heavily influenced the thinking that had shaped the dominant psychoanalytic theories.

Brenneman and Spitz (from Columbia) ran famous controlled studies in the foundling homes of New York City. They shocked the scientific world with their discovery—infants could die in an emotionally sterile world, deprived of comfort and affection. Gessel from Yale theorized that children develop by set sequential patterns whereby they can basically raise themselves. This notion, combined with analytic theory, colored the work and therapy of one of the earliest child guidance centers, the Langley-Porter Clinic at the University of California. This center espoused a permissive freedom of child development and remediation. On the opposite side of the country, Watson at Columbia espoused a compulsively ritualized schedule of child rearing that exhausted both mother and child. Kanner at Johns Hopkins later alleged that the unfortunate children raised under Watsonian psychology were found to have a two-and-a-half times higher rate of childhood schizophrenia than the general population.

Such were the early pains and claims of medically oriented psychiatry. Thankfully, new definitions have gradually evolved in the four areas of personality and behavior formation.

The first, biological, speaks of genetic inheritance, establishing both limits and potentials. Language and social behavior are defined within those limits.

The second, psychological, is defined as the perceptual, cognitive and affective development of personality structures as they relate to the individual and the environment.

Social structure, the third, refers to the way in which behavior becomes patterned and predictable. The institutions of social structure begin within the family and network out through a series of social structures defined by sex, race, ethnicity, stratifications, hierarch, authority, decision-making groups, economics and other factors. Each operates in a framework of cooperation or conflict.

The fourth, cultural, is defined as the milieu of interfacing processes involving concepts of value, morality, power, service, and a series of opposing forces. These are characterized by deviancy and conformity, rights and responsibilities, destruction or creativity and goal formation—positive or negative—with a culture seeking equilibrium between these forces.

In my years of training and practice, I have watched many theories and therapeutic approaches rise in popularity and then be abandoned. Enclaves and cults have sprung up, each claiming to have cornered scientific therapy. There are those who have stood firm for psychotherapy alone; and there's no question that such treatment provided by psychiatrists, psychologists and psychiatric social workers is extremely important. Physicians, on the other hand, have largely turned to therapeutic social workers and psychologists to bring about change in long-term therapy.

Many, in growing numbers and from several diagnostic categories, are responding solely or primarily to pharmacological preparations. These also have limits. The support system offered by adjunctive medications for other mental illnesses has caused us to rework our thinking with respect to cause, diagnosis and therapeutic delivery systems. It has also led to the use of better articulated interdisciplinary teams who deal with mental illness.

There have been major disappointments with some past therapies when they did not stand the tests of objective scientific research. Yet each has appeared to contribute some truth in the evolution of behavioral thought. The fact that we can always learn from what we have done is sometimes ignored when whole systems are discarded for a popular new theory. Perhaps that has been due to past practices based, frankly, on nonsense, unfounded faith, speculation, conjecture, distorted perception and emotional coloring. Such is the case of Freudian psychoanalytic theory.

We have also come to realize that modern childcare has added another level of problems. A recent report by Dr. Humberto Nagera, professor of child psychiatry at the University of Michigan, and his National Institute of Mental Health-appointed task force, reached startling conclusions in their exploration of daycare and other early childhood intervention programs, many of which tended to replace part or the majority of the family relationship. Dr. Nagera's task force concluded that the negative impact of poor daycare programs and childcare centers, along with the lack of early childhood developmental stimulation and education has been of such proportion that unless modified, the most basic elements of our nation and civilization are at risk.

Society's drawing away from the family, substituting the family, and marginalizing the family is creating a society poised for collapse as its framework is dismantled in the name of progress.

What they describe is already visible and causing damage. The family relationship of mother, father and child has already been seriously compromised.

In the early years of the 20th century, the pediatrician Dr. Joseph Brenneman visited orphanages in New York City. These foundling homes were for infants born out of wedlock or for very young orphans in their first two years of life. In those orphanages, he discovered a syndrome which was called, at the time, marasmus. Doctors thought it was a result of poor nutrition or infectious disease. Marasmus killed about 24 percent of the infants living in these quarters. In reality, their deaths were due to a lack of sufficient personnel to give care and attention to each one. Those who did not die carried the scars of irreversible intellectual and mental impairment.

Brenneman persuaded benefactors to fund and staff three facilities with extra personnel who would give tender, loving care and appropriate stimulation. The mortality rate dropped from 24 percent to

2 percent! Very convincing. This information shocked the scientific world. Suddenly, on the record was the proof that the life of a child is at risk if there is no appropriate emotional and loving care.

Though orphanages are not common today, what is common is a degree of damage to the central nervous system or brain due to a lack of loving personal, physical contact. This is usually found in the history of extreme conflict in dysfunctional homes, ones that lack the integrity of a true family unit, a home in which child abuse in all its forms—psychological, physical, sexual—rules. This abuse leaves the child with a resultant emotional and intellectual impairment which is carried into and throughout adulthood. Again, some of this damage to the normal brain may be irreversible.

Children who are deprived or abused first lose some of the development of their prefrontal cortex, the uniquely human part of the brain dealing with morals and values judgment and also decision making processes. The other loss is the linkage of the prefrontal cortex with the basal ganglia of the brain. The basal ganglia then chronically stimulates anxiety and gives rise to the pattern which we call post-traumatic stress disorder. Continuation of abnormal stimulation from the basal ganglia to the body, including the hormone system, also contributes to ongoing problems. It is hopeful to note here that in every child's developing brain there is a surplus of approximately 20 percent extra neurons in the frontal cortex that have yet to be formulated into functional neurons. They are in reserve to be developed—or not developed—in the adolescent years.

The impact of biochemically identified defects is being identified by advances in research. The biology of the child is being analyzed as to effects of psychological, social and cultural development, which includes morals and values. In addition, abnormalities of environment as the cause of biological changes manifest in developmental impairment are a key focus.

For example, deprivation and emotional stress can actually cause delays and defects in neural development. Environmental and academic demands can precipitate behavior maladjustments and syndromes. Those forces must be addressed in children and youth with biologically based developmental disabilities.

Some physicians have jumped to prescribe newer and more modern medications on a trial basis without establishing a follow-up plan. Very often such haphazard treatment ends up with poor results. The patient stops taking the medication because it doesn't work or the side-effects are so disturbing as to create a whole new list of problems. Other problems of child development resulting from ill-conceived therapy and well-meaning physicians who are not trained in such care and cannot draw from interdisciplinary association can cause difficulties in further treatment and recovery.

The therapeutic power of family ties

Medical science has never found anything which replaces the family. Society cannot escape the proof that the healthy development of children requires both a father and a mother. The amount of love given by a daycare center is no substitute, no matter what.

While many therapeutic programs have dismissed the importance of family in diagnosis and treatment, it is now becoming apparent that the most successful treatment programs acknowledge the family as essential to all functions of recovery beginning with history-taking through treatment and discharge.

It is clear that a combination of mental health specialties needs to come together in diagnosis as well as in therapeutic delivery systems, all in conjunction with family participation. To put it simply, both nature and nurture are important in healing our troubled youth. That means mental and emotional health must be addressed together because they each influence the other.

Chapter 14

From Self-Centered to Self-Esteem

". . . their souls are precious"

—Alma 31:35

ALL OF US ARE CHILDREN OF GOD. We have been born on earth at a time when the gospel is fully present. We also live in a time when most of the earth is covered in darkness and still the light of the gospel of Jesus Christ shines forth.

As a mental health professional, I rejoice in the spiritual support of the Church and in the guidance of the Holy Spirit so essential in my treatment of the ill. The direction of the Spirit is key to both preventive and curative needs of families.

In the course of my professional career, more than 50 years, I have watched mental and behavioral problems in society more than double. The published literature of mental health professionals has jumped more than two-and-a-half times in just the past two decades.

At issue for many is achieving a sense of self-worth, dignity and inner peace. These are safeguards to negative imprinting. A dysfunctional home, absence of a father or mother, or parents spending too little time with their children, are the staging ground for self-defeating imprints.

Self-image is important for children, youth and adults. As a package of personality, morals, values, virtues and talents, are we liked and accepted by others? Does it matter to us? What can we do to help our children reach a level of feeling good about themselves and how they relate to others?

Many would quickly respond, "Just build self-esteem and all will be well." The problem with that argument is that self-esteem often turns the emphasis inward toward self-centeredness. To help a child develop a happy and hopeful self-image requires turning outward. The path is one of Christ-like charity.

If charity abounds in the home, it will be emulated in years to come. Selfless devotion, love and care of parents are primary in shaping such an approach for a child or youth. They are the pattern for the child's marriage and for their own future families. The power and strength of a healthy self-image can be passed from generation to generation confirming that by "losing ourselves in the service of others," we find ourselves.

Several years ago I was assigned with Brigham Young University professor Dr. Neil Flinders to help develop curriculum materials for the Church on morals and values. We drew upon the studies, experience and teaching of professors from Oxford and Cambridge Universities in England and from professors at Harvard University, specifically Dr. Lawrence Kohlberg. His expertise was teaching morals and values in public schools.

Is it curious that we reached outside the Church population for expertise? Not at all. These were learned professionals who had determined, without the benefit of the gospel plan, that morals and values were central to a positive self-image.

Dr. Kohlberg visited BYU and met with professors from several disciplines including the Department of Religion. Although his background was Jewish, he was impressed with the Church's emphasis on morals and ethics reaching beyond the Golden Rule. He recognized the Church's emulation of Jesus Christ in leading the world to loving service of others without expecting personal reward. In his estimation, Church members had reached the highest level of morals and values.

In referring to his own Jewish culture, he recalled how it was customary for parents to tell their children that they were endowed with greater intelligence and superiority than others in the neighborhood or even the world. He stated that this particular approach was not a dogma of Judaism but rather an interpretation of individual members who considered themselves more "choice" than "chosen," often leading to self-centeredness rather than self-worth.

Self-esteem is a byproduct of wholesome living. It is not the end goal or the end result nor is it the "golden road" to mental health. If youth are taught to help others only to find personal satisfaction, the cause is vain. Lavishing children with praise for personal moral qualities as a means of increasing their self-esteem is ineffective and does not boost confidence. Rather, it inhibits them from performing future acts without certainty of success. Confidence is not built by talk. Good self-image is a product of truthful appreciation of genuine skills and the sheer pleasure of helping others.

The wonderful array of programs in the Church offer youth the opportunity to serve others in many ways. As they lose themselves for others, they find themselves. Inspired by the Lord, this approach prepares youth when they come of age to serve a mission—for the Lord. When successful, self-centered personality patterns disappear and preparation for adulthood is the next step.

Most literature on mental health addresses treatment and neglects prevention. While professionals cry out for intervention to save those with adverse childhood experiences (and there's no question that treatment is advisable for those with a past history of some form of abuse or family challenges, depression, chronic anxiety and personality disorders, substance abuse and even predisposition for suicide), I've found that preventive measures and strategies that address cultural and family patterns is far more effective in stemming the rise of negative imprinting raging among youth today.

The gospel of Jesus Christ has the answers. All the truths of the gospel strengthen families. As reiterated in The Family: A Proclamation to the World: "Happiness in family life is most likely to be achieved when founded upon the teachings of the Lord Jesus Christ. Successful marriages and families are established and maintained on principles of faith, prayer, repentance, forgiveness, respect, love, compassion, work, and wholesome recreational activities."

Clearly, prevention begins with the eternal marriage goal of man and wife. Regular prayer surrounding the conception, birth, and raising of a child is essential for "Children are an heritage of the Lord" (Psalms 127:3).

What a thrill to see my grandchildren, now moms and dads themselves, spend a generous share of their time in personal care and play with my great grandchildren. Bonding takes place and self-esteem is established by the unwritten messages, "You are important. . . I like you. . .This is a good way to spend our time. . ."

Individual attention is essential by all generations of the family. Extended Family Home Evenings and holiday celebrations are always an asset to building self-esteem. Children then learn that the morals, values and standards taught by their parents are multi-generational. They are blessed by the testimonies and power of the priesthood in all generations.

If children have these experiences in infancy, if they become engaged themselves as young toddlers, if they find a circle of support around them as a child, then group and individual advice or direction are more easily accepted and acted upon in adolescence.

The fundamental principle of all social systems is the family. As the world wrestles with that understanding, the positive imprint of family will sustain and secure our youth and children to the hope of the future. As our children are taught to look outward, serving others with the pure love of Christ (rather than looking inward which only feeds self-centeredness), they will find lasting self-worth.

Chapter 15

Why the Family Is the Answer

"God's government in time as well as in eternity
is family government."

—*Joseph Smith, Jr.*

By 2010, THERE WILL BE APPROXIMATELY 35 MILLION YOUTH in this country between the ages of 12-19. How they feel, act, and deal with others and with themselves, and how they shoulder their place in leadership in the home and in the communities in which they live will either sustain the best of society or lead to a devastating decline of a great and noble people.

From his dream, the Book of Mormon prophet Lehi described, "A mist of darkness covered the land." We have a mist all about us today. But Lehi also saw in vision the tree of life and he "partook of the fruit" and his soul "was filled with exceeding great joy." Partaking of the fruit alone, however, was not enough. "I began to be desirous," he wrote, "that my family should partake of it also." Such righteous purpose, the growth of families as they prepare to "come unto Christ," cannot be dismissed by the fashion of the day. With "the feeling of a tender parent," Lehi taught his family the truths of the gospel of Jesus Christ.

So it is today. Parents have a "sacred duty to rear their children in love and righteousness, to provide for their physical and spiritual needs, to teach them to love and serve one another, to observe the commandments of God and to be law-abiding citizens wherever they live" (The Family: A Proclamation to the World).

Fathers and mothers have been duped into thinking that parenting merely means guiding adolescents through the formation of a value system largely shaped by peers and by the permutations of society. Many have even espoused the false belief that it is wrong or "too controlling" to create and enforce structure, expectations, and family values. Children are no longer seen as young men and women in training. In other words, they have lost their moorings. In their place have come a host of negative imprints. Family plays a key role in feeding and sustaining a well-wired brain. The lack of strong family values, family talk, and family time is a clear invitation for negative imprinting.

Look at what we are facing. Homes are fragmented—fathers work; mothers work; youth attend school, take lessons, play sports and tend each other. Frequently a home-cooked meal means one warmed in the microwave. The "home-fires" have given way to a fantasy-addicted, highly manipulated teen populace connected to practically every form of media. The undermining of a faithful culture is the plague of today. Add divorce to already broken lives and the "survivor" instinct—not the media-packaged "Survivor" but the real day-to-day one—takes over and adds another layer of desperate times to an already burdened child.

A permissive philosophy is raging across this country and world, working to negate and diminish the concept of family. In many camps, defense of the family has become politically incorrect. A frightening number of churchmen, sociologists and psychologists are giving evidence to support a belief that the family is a dying institution. In truth, the family is ordained of God and no mere mortal can reconfigure what is divine.

We know that the fundamental unit of society is indisputably the family. For many, that may be an image that is fading or simply eclipsed by notions of political correctness. Not only church and government are based on this foundation. In a healthy society all programs, both political and ecclesiastical, converge on the family. The family has direction—an eternal path.

The family has two fundamental purposes and is incomplete if it neglects either. The first is to provide a relationship whereby a person is fulfilled. A man is not really a fulfilled creature or a unified creature unless he has a marriage relationship to a woman. Nor is a woman fulfilled unless she has a man in her family association. It could be said this way: A man alone is only half a person; a woman alone is only half as well. Put them together, however, and a super-individual—more complete than one individual or two—is formed.

The second fundamental purpose of the family unit is that it exists to rear children. If there are no children in the home, some feel it cannot correctly be called a family. Yet grandparents and newlyweds are family. The definition and purpose of the family cannot be construed by the numbers living in the home.

The family unit is one defined by love, extended by love, supported and configured by love. Without love, a child will die. That love is expressed in a host of terms—affection, adoration, security, protection, safety, friendship, guidance, patience, generosity, appreciation, and respect—to name a few. A child must have love; it is as necessary as food. Without love, a child or youth must manufacture all kinds of psychological defenses. Tragically for some, they carry the imprint of neglect and abuse and the brain goes totally wrong.

In the last century, research in the behavioral sciences has found that the seeds of a variety of personality disorders are established in early childhood. There they are sown. Behavioral scientists have determined that there is a clear correlation between the early child/parent relationship and a whole range of problems from delinquency and aggression to various forms of moral and social conflict. Indeed, it would be surprising if this were not the case. The influence of parents brought to bear at the most impressionable periods of a child and teenager's life is bound to be significant. This is what gives family a special and significant role in society.

In parenting, we create a fixed wiring of the child for future developmental processes. What a great blessing to not be operating in a "mist of darkness," but rather in the light of Christ. Through the teachings of the gospel of Jesus Christ and supported by the Church of Jesus Christ of Latter-day Saints, we can raise our children and love them in an appropriate, God-directed way.

The gospel plan and its influence in our families can prompt respectful association. The overtones should be ones of concern and caring, open communication and interest. We can model sharing, honest pleasure in another's success, forgiveness, devotion and honor. Integrity—honesty, reliability, virtue, and trust—can be the measure of our family life. As we show consideration for our youth's feelings, for their privacy and their participation, we are modeling behavior they will take with them from the home into the world. There is no place for anger, abuse, or manipulation in a righteous home.

Time spent with family is the most precious time on earth. When we take the family fishing or to a ball game, when we join together to bake treats for the neighborhood picnic or sit on the backyard swing, we are shaping patterns that will outlive us. It is not the nature of the activity that is important, but it is the sharing of experiences together that will make the difference.

The idea of "together time" has lost some of its power in our hectic world. Getting together for orchestrated holiday celebrations is important. Equally dramatic is the influence of casual time when children and youth spontaneously join with family—parents, grandparents, aunts, uncles and cousins. No child or youth will object to one-on-one time with mom or dad. Just a trip to the store can bring a sense of belonging and love.

A young man, away from home on a mission, wrote home of his struggles. He concluded with these words, "I take comfort in the great times we had as a family at home. I am going to be okay."

The LDS Church's Family Home Evening program is designed to get families together talking, playing, eating, and enjoying one another's company. Family home evenings should be instituted early in the marriage. In fact, many Church leaders encourage it to bond a young couple even before children have come into the home. Family Home Evening is an environment where parents "gather their children about them in love and patience and understanding and instruct them in truth and righteousness and teach them correct principles by the words they speak and by the example of their lives."

Many of the subjects in this book would make good discussion topics for family home evening, particularly with families of teens. Don't be afraid to address sensitive social issues; your youth are addressing them every day and need your help!

Equally as important as the topics discussed in family gatherings, is the atmosphere in which that discussion takes place. Love, patience, understanding and acceptance are central to any healthy interchange. Everyone needs to feel free to participate, to say what he feels like saying without fear of recrimination. The tone, relaxed and comfortable, needs to be inviting to each member of the family.

For example, a family with children stretching in age from 7 to 15 gathered for family time one evening. They spoke of love for one another, a subject that seemed appropriate for the tugs on family relationships. Each was asked to identify three things that family members could do to help them feel loved. The youngest, a bold and seemingly independent boy, reported just one thought from his list: "To know there is someone there for me." There was quiet in the room as the older siblings looked at him. Such a revealing statement was a commentary on his trust in the family.

Decision making is never completely comfortable, but in the home, when decisions are put to the family, consensus needs to be reached, so that all can support the decision. Formal voting should be held to a minimum and the family should never accept simple majority as a proper basis for action. What becomes important here is not the decision itself but the way in which it was reached. Decisions by consensus bind a family together. Decisions by majority split families.

When action is taken, clear assignments should be made and accepted. Very often it is a good idea to repeat again what has been said so that it is clear what has been accepted and what is expected.

Every idea should be given a complete hearing. No family member should be afraid of looking foolish by putting forth a creative thought, even it seems to be fairly extreme at the time. Premature censorship is far too common in many family discussions.

Finally, parents should be on guard not to dominate the discussions. Hence the name, Family Home Evening. A private discussion is not just for mom, dad or the child, but is a combined instrument of communication.

When this type of atmosphere accompanies the family, the home evening, or the individual relationships with children on other occasions, there is no "generation gap." Everyone feels an integral part of the group and its operation; but parents, with their years of experience and understanding at work, must initiate such an atmosphere. It cannot be left to develop as a matter of course.

The key to success still lies with that overworked word "Communication." Some interpret it to mean "speak at" rather than "speak with." If we effectively communicate the truth to our youth, then in a few short years when we can no longer carry the standard, they will be prepared, even eager, to pick it up. They will have found that communication has existed not only in their family, but has come about in their relationship with the Lord.

Love at home is not a 1950s sitcom outdated by today's standards. It is the cradle of positive imprinting. Togetherness, support and belonging blunt the desire to try something, "just this once." Families need to be led by parents. For families to make a difference, to be a reservoir of strength and purpose, they must meet four structured needs:

- Keep in contact—know the comings and goings, the friends, the pressures.
- Be together as often as possible—dinner, family night, morning prayer, evening wrap-up.
- Be genuinely concerned about the welfare of family members.
- Talk—and keep talking.

- Rally when one is floundering.
- Reach back to those who have gone before. Although society and even education have turned their backs on greatness, family histories are replete with records of men and women who struggled to rise above meager existence. The birthright of every youth is grounded in the great deeds of those who had faith when life was hopeless, who fortified reason against unreason, and who stood for justice, God-given purpose and vision. This is what we call heritage, and it has worth beyond date, time and place.

Positive imprinting is the goal. Our youth can stand up to the negative influences that slyly draw them off. A support system can bring them back, one positive imprint at a time.

Conclusion

The premise I've set forth in this text is not unique to LDS thinking or LDS physicians. Nobel Prize-winning scientist Dr. LeComte du Nouy, whose acclaimed study of the physiology and neurological functioning of the human brain supports these conclusions. He too has determined that the uniqueness of the prefrontal cortex in human beings places them in distinct contrast to the animal world. In fact, he avows that there is a greater evolutionary leap from the brain of animal to man than there is from the comparison of inorganic to organic. He suggests that the quantum leap between animals and humans is so great that mankind is the "only creation in the universe with the freedom of choice and the liberty of conscience." His studies show that those who follow their conscience and exercise their choice of liberty in relation to morals and values as well as decision making, reach higher plains of behavior, moral growth and development. If they engage in behaviors that negatively impact their brains such as substance abuse and resultant dependency, they can expect loss of prefrontal functioning—the characteristic unique to mankind. Addiction indulgence, he contends, creates an indifference to spirituality as well.

Famed psychiatrist Dr. Karl Jung, an associate and friend of Dr. Nouy, has made similar conclusions. Both believe in the beneficial effects of religion, spirituality, prayer and faith in the growth and development of the human being as well as the restoration of what I call "a brain gone wrong." Dr. Nouy states that superiority of the human brain can be manifested by "a will bent toward an ideal of untiring effort to draw near to God." In summary, he asks, "Is this not in reality a prayer, a creed or a means of expressing faith in the dignity of man as he addresses his own personal self and reaches beyond him to a God whose wisdom is given freely to us if we have a normal and optimal functioning brain with its uniquely human prefrontal cortex?"

The greatest battle for our youth is fought within. Taking control begins with setting aside pleasure for peace. Adolescents must find personal definition as a child of a loving Father in Heaven. They must come to know for themselves that he has chosen for us to address him as Father, that the intimate relationship of father and child is real and lasting. God's plan is not driven by rewards or punishments; it is one of consequences. Those whose lives have been driven by addiction have lost sight of cause and effect. Yet those who have mastered addiction in any of its forms, who have restored their God-given gift of a brain that can think and reason and make sound judgments, who have learned enduring to the end is not a darkened tunnel but a brilliant path, are poised to step forward, taking control of their lives, trusting to another day.

About the Author

Dr. W. Dean Belnap is a specialist in pediatrics and child/adolescent psychiatry who obtained his medical degree at the University of Utah, with post-graduate training at the University of Utah, Case Western Reserve and Harvard University Schools of Medicine.

He is a Fellow of the American Academy of Pediatrics, the American Psychiatric Association, the Society of Behavioral Pediatrics, the American Society of Adolescent Psychiatry, and the American Neuropsychiatric Association.

Dr. Belnap has been in private practice and on the clinical faculty at the University of Utah Medical School. He has been involved in local and state public health and community mental health agencies, and has served as the director of nationwide psychiatric hospitals. He has also been elected to local and state boards of education.

His professional appointments include the School Health Committee of the American Medical Association and the Handicapped Children's Committee of the American Academy of Pediatrics. He has served as an officer of the National School Boards Association. During Pres. Ronald Reagan's administration, he was appointed to serve on the Advisory Council of the Department of Health and Human Services.

Church and humanitarian service assignments have taken him to many parts of the world for extended periods of time. He has written many articles that have been published in various medical journals, and has also enjoyed publishing books for parents and their posterity. He co-authored two books with Dr. Glen Griffin: About Life and Love, a guide for parents and adolescents, and About Marriage and More, a resource for couples anticipating marriage. He also authored Raising Families in Our Permissive Society and Heritage with Honor. His book, *Matters of the Mind,* co-authored with Dr. Marleen Williams and Dr. John Livingstone, will be released Fall of 2008.